Companion Manual

to

A Conceptual Approach to Teaching Children About Science, Technology, and Society

Brenda J. Gustafson, Ph.D.
Dougal A. G. MacDonald, Ph.D.

Ripon Publishing 2005
A Division of Ripon Consulting Ltd.
ISBN: 6-0153-0015-9

Also available by the same authors: A Conceptual Approach to Teaching Children About Science,
Technology, and Society (2005).
Ripon Publishing: A Division of Ripon Consulting Ltd.
ISBN: 6-0153-0014-0

A discount is provided when ordering the combined publication package, which includes the main textbook and this
accompanying Companion Manual.
Contact: RiponPub@telus.net

[Library of Congress Info]
ISBN: 6-0153-0015-9

The Web addresses cited in this text were current as of June 2005, unless otherwise noted.

Acquisitions Editor: Dr. G. J. Fishburne; **Developmental Editor:** Dr. G. J. Fishburne; **Copyeditor:** Dr. G. J. Fishburne; **Cover Designer:** Chad Spears; **Text Layout:** Sara Bartisch

Printed in Edmonton, Alberta, Canada by Dial Printing Inc.

Ripon Publishing
RipPub@Telus.net

Copyright Protected

About the Authors

Dr. Brenda Gustafson began her career as an elementary school teacher and is now a Professor of Elementary Science Education at the University of Alberta. Dr. Gustafson has been awarded the Faculty of Education's Undergraduate Teaching award for her distinguished teaching and has presented many workshops and seminars for elementary teachers. Her research has focused on teaching science and design technology in elementary classrooms. She has published in academic journals such as the Journal of Technology Education, Research in Science Education, the Journal of Qualitative Studies in Education, the Canadian Journal of Science, Mathematics and Technology Education, Research in Science and Technology Education, the International Journal of Technology and Design Education, and the Alberta Journal of Education Research. She has presented her research at numerous annual conferences such as those associated with the Canadian Society for the Study of Education, the American Educational Research Association, The International Technology Education Association, and the National Association for Research in Science Teaching.

Dr. Dougal MacDonald is an award-winning full-time sessional instructor at the University of Alberta where he currently teaches elementary science methods. A science educator for over 17 years, he is known for his enthusiasm, sense of humour, and ability to meaningfully integrate theory and practice. Dougal's main research interests are constructivism, the conceptual analysis of teaching, the nature of science, Aboriginal education, and design technology. His research has been presented at international conferences and published in international academic journals.

Special Note

A portion of the proceeds from this book will be donated to undergraduate student awards in education.

Disclaimer: Safety and Teaching Progressions

All the activities contained in this textbook have been identified as developmentally appropriate for children and youth, providing recognized teaching progressions are followed, and recognized safety procedures adhered to and employed. Before engaging in any of the activities, or teaching any of the activities identified in this textbook, the reader must be familiar with and cognizant of both recognized safety considerations and developmentally appropriate teaching progressions, and must follow these safety considerations and teaching progressions. Hence, anyone who engages in any of the activities contained in this textbook does so completely at their own risk. Anyone who engages in any of the activities contained or suggested in this textbook takes full responsibility for any and all effects as a result of engaging in these activities. No blame, fault, or liability whatsoever of any kind can be made against the authors of this publication or the publishing company Implementation of any of the activities or ideas contained in this textbook should in all cases be preceded by a close review of the specific requirements and circumstances associated with the teaching, learning, and/or performing situation. Each person using the activities and ideas contained in this textbook assumes the risks associated with the implementation and customization of the activities and ideas. The authors, editors, and publishing company make no representations or warranties, either expressed or implied, as to any matter including the condition, quality, or freedom from error of the activities, ideas, and content contained in this textbook. Each person using the activities, ideas, and content assumes the risk of defects or inaccuracies in the textbook as supplied by the authors, editors, and publishing company. The authors, editor, and publishing company will have no liability, consequential damages, special damages, punitive damages, or otherwise which might arise from the use by any one of the activities, ideas, and content material contained within this textbook.

Safety Guidelines

When teaching or engaging people in the activities and ideas contained in this textbook, recognized safety guidelines must be followed. Check and follow the safety guidelines policy and procedures applicable to the school district, municipality, county, province, state, and country where the teaching of the activities and ideas contained in this textbook will occur. As noted above, when people participate in activities there is a risk of injury. Therefore teachers must be careful to provide an adequate standard of care for the people they are teaching; that is, they must create safe learning environments. Prior to teaching or engaging people in the activities and ideas contained in this textbook, teachers must be able to answer each of the following five questions with a 'yes' :

1. Is the activity suitable to the age, cognitive, emotional, and physical condition of the participants? In other words is it developmentally appropriate?

2. Will the participants be taught through correct teaching progressions, and do the teacher's unit and lesson plans indicate and support this?

3. Are the apparatus, equipment, and materials developmentally appropriate, suitably arranged for a safe learning environment, and in good condition?

4. Will the activity be supervised properly?

5. Has a 'risk' assessment been made to consider the potential risks associated with the planned activities? And have 'safety' steps been taken to reduce or minimize these risks?

Teaching in Alberta Schools

The following 'safety' guideline is recommended and must be followed when teaching or engaging children and youth in any type of physical activity in Alberta Schools in Canada:

Safety Guidelines
For Physical Activity in Alberta Schools
ISBN 0-9699567-6-2

Web site: *www.med.ualberta.ca/acicr*
This web site provides links to resources (safety guidelines, policies, procedures, recommendations, etc.) across Canada and the United States.
Many resource recommendations are available on line through the web site, including the following documents:

Safety Guidelines for Physical Activity in Alberta Schools
L'activite physique dans les ecole de l'Alberta (available in electronic version only)
ACICR Bicycle Education Program Inventory
Thesaurus of Injury Prevention Terminology
Safety Guidelines for Secondary Interschool Athletics in Alberta
The Alberta Directory for Emergency Medical and Acute Care Services
Alberta Education: Safety in the Science Classroom
www.education.gov.ab.ca

Inquiries can be addressed to:
Alberta Centre for Injury Control & Research
University of Alberta, 4075 EDC,
8308 – 114 Street, Edmonton, Alberta, Canada T6G 2V2
Tel: 780-492-7154

Contents

Part A: Activities Related to Textbook Chapters

Part B: Sample Activities for Classroom Work

Scientific Inquiry Activities

Technological Problem-Solving Activities

STS Decision-Making Activities

Part C: Overview of Subject Matter Knowledge and Typical Classroom Activities

Physical Science

Life Science

Earth and Space Science

Technological Structures and Devices

Nature of and Relationships Between Science and Technology

Social and Environmental Contexts of Science and Technology

Part D: Concepts Related to the Alberta Elementary Science Program Topics

Grade 1

Grade 2

Part E: Growing Professionally

Part A
Activities Related to the Textbook Chapters

Chapter 1
Introduction To Teaching Children About Science, Technology, and Society

Textbook Activity 1.1

A View of Scientists

Draw a picture of a scientist; then answer the following questions:

- Where did you get your ideas about scientists?
- How does the image of the scientist in your drawing compare with your classmates' drawings?
- How would you help a child develop an understanding of diversity among scientists?

Textbook Activity 1.2

The Nature of Science

Read the following story that tells of the evidence available for analysis after an event has occurred:
A child discovers one morning that her dog is missing. The gate to the fence is open. The gate appears not to have been forced open. There are tire tracks leading up to the gate, but there are no dog footprints outside the fence. There are some rabbit footprints in a flowerbed inside the yard and some pieces of dog food left in the yard.

Now answer the following questions:

- What might you guess happened to the dog?
- How do you decide what is the best hypothesis?
- How could you test your hypothesis?
- How can you relate this activity to the description of science provided in Chapter 1?

Textbook Activity 1.3

A Child's View of Science

Talk with a child about how he or she views science, and then answer the following questions:

- How are the child's views similar to or different from how science has been described in the previous sections of this text?
- Where did the child get his or her ideas about science?
- What do the child's words imply about how we should teach science? about how we should talk about science?

Textbook Activity 1.4

Analyzing a Science Teaching Resource

Research shows that science teaching resources (e.g., science textbooks and science curriculum programs) contain messages about why we should be teaching science to children. Sometimes these messages are explicitly stated; other times they are found "between the lines." As a teacher, you need to be alert to such messages in your classroom resources. Your students will perceive them, perhaps unconsciously, and be influenced by them. If the messages don't present a balanced view, your students' view of science may be correspondingly distorted.

For this activity, examine a commonly used science teaching resource, and then answer the following questions:

- What does the cover of the book look like? What does it suggest science is all about?
- What kinds of illustrations does the book have? What do you notice about the people depicted? What image of science and scientists do these illustrations suggest?
- What views of science are presented or implied?
- What views are presented or implied about why children should be taught science?
- In what ways are these views about science and about why it should be taught to children similar to or different from the views presented so far in this textbook?.

Textbook Activity 1.5

Benefits of Scientific Literacy

Think of a time in your life when knowledge of science would have helped you in any of the ways listed in chapter 1 – perhaps to make a more informed purchase or to engage in public debate in a more informed manner. Then answer the following questions:

- What knowledge would have helped you out?
- How could you have gained this knowledge?
- What else besides scientific knowledge influenced the stance you took or the decisions you made?
- What ideas do you have for helping your future students move towards scientific literacy?
- How might you and your students benefit from discussing the meaning of scientific literacy?

Textbook Activity 1.6

A Comprehensive View of Technology

Read several different accounts on the Worldwide Web of the story of how Thomas Edison invented the light bulb, then answer the following questions:

- What knowledge did Edison require?

- How would you describe Edison's processes of design?

- What role did the social context play in Edison's invention?

Textbook Activity 1.7

Images of Science and Technology in the Alberta Elementary Science Program

Part A: Topic Arrangement and Emphases

In your *Alberta Elementary Science Program* (1996), find the list of topics for Grade 4 and their accompanying emphases. Read the list of Grade 4 topics and then answer the following questions:

- What image of the relative importance of technology to science might be suggested by the topic list?

- What image of the relationship between science and technology might be suggested by the connection between Science Inquiry and Problem Solving Through Technology topics?

Part B: Science Inquiry and Problem Solving Through Technology

Look at the two models for Grade 4 (Science Inquiry and Problem Solving Through Technology) that are presented on pages B.17 and B.18 in your program document. An assumption made in the presentation of these two models is that the processes or skills of technological problem solving are similar to those found in scientific inquiry. In your textbook, however, the authors argue that the purposes of scientific inquiry and technological problem-solving are different and therefore, the skills associated with each are also somewhat different.

- What would you add to these models in order to help children distinguish scientific inquiry from technological problem-solving?

Part C Topic Learner Expectations

Read through the General Learner Expectations and the Specific Learner Expectations that are listed under *Topic 4C Building Devices and Vehicles That Move.*

- What is the image of the relationship between technology and society suggested in the learner expectations?

Chapter 2
Children's Learning in STS

Textbook Activity 2.1

Thinking About Children's Alternative Conceptions of the Structure and Properties of Matter

Select one of the alternative conceptions listed below. Search the Internet to find out how scientists' ideas differ from the children's conception; then answer the following questions:

- What is the intelligent thinking that resulted in the selected alternative conception?
- In what ways do scientists' ideas differ from the children's alternative conception?
- How would you help a child with the selected alternative conception move towards understanding scientists' ideas?

Children's Alternative Conceptions

CONCEPT AREA: FLOATING AND SINKING

- Light objects float; heavy objects sink.
- Objects on top of the water are held up by the water's skin.
- An object is floating only if part of it is above the water; submerged objects are not floating.

CONCEPT AREA: CHEMICAL CHANGE

- Ice melting to water is a chemical change because ice and water are different substances.
- When fuel burns it "disappears."
- The products of a chemical reaction are inside the starting materials.
- A chemical reaction involves a fizz or an explosion.

Textbook Activity 2.2

Thinking About How Sound Travels

Look at the list of children's alternative conceptions listed below; then answer the following questions:

- How do you think a child might come to the conclusion that "bigger vibrations are slower than smaller vibrations"?
- Why do you think a child would believe that "sound can travel only if there is nothing in the way"?
- Look at two or three children's science textbooks. How do they show sound waves traveling from a source?
- How might these textbook illustrations help or hinder children's understanding of how sound travels?

Children's Alternative Conceptions

CONCEPT AREA: SOUND ENERGY

- Sound is produced by the physical properties of the material.
- Vibration has nothing to do with the production of sound.
- Sound can only travel if there is nothing in the way.
- Bigger vibrations are slower than smaller vibrations.

Textbook Activity 2.3

Thinking About Rock Coloration

In a study by Symington, Biddulph, Happs, and Osborne (1982), children explained why rocks had different colors. Two children commented that:

- The rocks grew like that. We're different colors—white people, black people. Different colors and different soils.
- The sun makes the color of rocks light, like one hair gets lighter in color in the summer.

Now answer the following questions:

- How do these explanations show children using their existing knowledge to explain scientific phenomena?
- What kinds of reasoning did the children use to justify their ideas about rock coloration?
- How would you relate your ideas to the constructivist view of learning?
- How would you help children who believed these explanations move towards a scientific understanding of rock coloration?

Textbook Activity 2.4

Thinking About Heat and Temperature

Read the ideas about heat and temperature listed below.

Children's Alternative Conceptions

CONCEPT AREA: HEAT ENERGY

- Heat is a substance.
- The temperature of an object is based more on the nature of the material than on the temperature of the surrounding medium.
- Temperature is related to size.
- The temperature of a boiling liquid continues to rise.

Search the Internet to find basic scientific ideas about heat and temperature; then answer the following questions:

- What does temperature measure?
- What is heat energy?
- How would you help children distinguish between heat and temperature?
- Why do you think some children use the terms "heat" and "temperature" interchangeably in everyday life?

Textbook Activity 2.5

Thinking About Everyday Explanations and Scientific Explanations

In everyday life, people say, "The sun rises in the morning and sets at night." In science class, we teach students that the earth turns on its axis once every 24 hours, resulting in day and night and the apparent movement of the sun. Solomon (1983) argues that science teachers should understand that both explanations have their place in students' lives and that it is not necessary to insist that students replace their everyday explanations with the scientific explanations; instead, teachers should realize that students who are able to move back and forth between the two explanations and who understand how each is a reasonable way to talk about night and day are becoming scientifically literate. Answer the following questions:

- Do you agree or disagree with Solomon's argument? Why?
- How do Solomon's ideas contrast with those of other researchers, who argue that teachers must use a variety of teaching strategies designed to help children replace their alternative conceptions?
- How would you decide whether to challenge children's alternative conceptions or to help children understand that these conceptions might be appropriate in some contexts?

Textbook Activity 2.6

Drawing Pictures of Children's Alternative Conceptions of Electrical Energy

Look at the three children's alternative conceptions listed below. Draw pictures to illustrate each of the alternative conceptions; then answer the following questions about helping children move towards more scientific ideas:

- How would you use your illustrations to talk with a child who believed the first or second alternative conception?
- How would you use your illustration along with hands-on materials such as batteries, bulbs, and wires to talk with a child who believed the third alternative conception?

Children's Alternative Conceptions

CONCEPT AREA: ELECTRICAL ENERGY

- Only one wire is required for a complete circuit; the second wire is a safety wire.
- Current flows from both ends of the battery and meets at a bulb.
- A bulb "uses up" current, so the part of a circuit after the bulb will have less current than the part before it.

Textbook Activity 2.7

A Conversation With a Child

Here is part of a transcript from a lesson on buoyancy conducted with one Grade Two student (T = Teacher, C = Child). The child hypothesized that objects float because they are light and sink because they are heavy. The child was then given a set of objects and asked to predict which ones would sink and which ones would float. The child placed the objects one by one in water to test her predictions.

T: See if you can see what made all the sinkers sink and all the floaters float.

C: Hmmm (examining objects). It's heavy?

T: It's heavy and was that heavy one a sinker or a floater?

C: A sinker.

T: A sinker, okay.

C: It went to the bottom.

T: Is that the only thing about them? Are they all heavy?

C: No, this one's light.

T: Hmm, that one's light.

C: But it still sinks.

T: Why in the world would that be?

C: Cause...it's little?

T: Okay.

C: And these are sort of heavy and sort of light.

T: The marble. Was it a sinker too?

C: Uh huh, because they're...they're little?

T: Okay, sure.

C: The hockey puck...

T: Yes, what do you think about that one?

C: Because it is fat.

T: He's fat so he sunk?

C: (Nods).

T: Why did you think he'd float? You had him down there as a floater (points to prediction).

C: Cause he's...he's heavy.

T: Okay.

C: Some heavy things float and some don't.

T: Oh, okay.

C: And this one is a sinker (indicates screwdriver).

T: And why would that one sink.

C: Because it's skinny.

Now answer the following questions.

From where do you think the child got the idea that light objects float and heavy objects sink?

- How have the sink-float tests changed the child's ideas about why some objects float and some sink? Evidence?

- How would you characterize the child's new explanation of sinking and floating?

- How is the child's reasoning similar to and different from a scientist? Evidence?

- If you were the teacher what would you do next to try to help the child better understand why objects float or sink?

Chapter 3
Building Blocks of STS:
Concepts, Skills,
and Attitudes

Textbook Activity 3.1

Teachers' Beliefs About Science

Read the following descriptions of three teachers' beliefs about science. Then, answer the questions.

TEACHER A

This teacher believes that science is a body of knowledge. "Science," she says, "is chemistry, biology, and physics."

How do you think a teacher with this belief about the nature of science would teach science to elementary children?

TEACHER B

This teacher believes that science is all about learning skills such as observation, prediction, classification, and hypothesizing.

How do you think a teacher with this belief about the nature of science would teach science to elementary children?

TEACHER C

This teacher believes that science is all about children discovering science ideas for themselves.

How do you think a teacher with this belief about the nature of science would teach science to elementary children?

Textbook Activity 3.2

Thinking About Skills and Conceptual Knowledge

In the 1960s, Robert Gagne suggested that in order to carry out effective scientific inquiry students first needed to learn skills such as observing, classifying, inferring, and interpreting data. Students could then use these learned skills to inductively develop conceptual knowledge from sensory experience, i.e., students could develop knowledge by:

- Observing and collecting facts (e.g., testing the following materials with a magnet—plastic comb, wooden ruler, ribbon, steel nail, piece of cardboard, eraser, scrap iron, ceramic tile, glass microscope slide).

- Analyzing and classifying facts (e.g., classifying materials as magnetic or non-magnetic).

- Deriving generalizations from facts (e.g., generalizing that metals are magnetic).

- Further testing the generalizations (e.g., testing a steel washer and a steel bolt).

Now answer the following question:

- Why might a student conclude from the above activity that metals are magnetic?

- Are metals magnetic? How do you know?

- What materials are magnetic? How do you know?

- How does this example show that a skills-first approach misleads students as to the critical role of conceptual knowledge in scientific reasoning?

Textbook Activity 3.3

Thinking About Concepts

Read the following list of concepts:

- Biological classification takes into account the diversity of life on Earth.

- Living things have different life cycles.

- Reproduction is a characteristic of all living systems.

- Living things have features that enable them to meet their needs (eyes collect visual information).

- Offspring tend to resemble their parents.

- Animals can be grouped according to common characteristics (e.g., vertebrates and invertebrates; mammals, birds, reptiles, amphibians and fishes).

- Habitat loss and adaptive capability can affect population size and existence.

- Environmental changes can occur naturally or be influenced by humans (e.g., through erosion, urban growth and waste disposal).

- Animal life cycles can be classified according to similarities and differences (e.g., life cycles of insects, amphibians and reptiles are similar in some ways and different in others).

- Extinction of species is common.

- Animals have features that enable them to meet their needs in special places (e.g., some aquatic animals have gills and others have webbed feet).

- Animal offspring generally look like their parent(s) but can differ in some ways.

- Environments are subject to change.

Arrange the above concepts into a web that shows connections between concepts and the nature of the relationship between the concepts.

Textbook Activity 3.4

Thinking About Skills

Read the scenario, and then answer the following questions.

Grade 4 children are hiking with their teacher through a lightly wooded area adjacent to the schoolyard. Their teacher has planned that the children watch for signs of spring in anticipation of her next science unit on *Plant Growth and Changes.*

One child comments that she can smell a damp, moldy smell and exclaims that it must be the leaves underfoot. A second child notices that no grass appears to be growing underneath the spruce trees. He comments that there must be some kind of substance that rains down from the spruce trees that prevents other plants from growing. A third child draws attention to the increasing cloud cover and comments that it is likely to rain tomorrow. A fourth child points to some green plants beginning to emerge from the soil and says that he cannot recall the name of the plant but knows that it features frond-like leaves, with brown dots underneath the leaves, and people can boil it and eat it during the early stages of its growth. A fifth child bends down to record the height of the plants and remarks that the plant reminds her of other similar plants that also have frond-like leaves. A sixth child adds that it is unlikely that all plants with frond-like leaves can be eaten safely by people.

- What skills did the children appear to use as they participated in the hike?

- How were the skills guided by the students' existing conceptions?

- How would you assist the children to understand that the skills used were not unique to a science context?

Textbook Activity 3.5

Thinking About Attitudes

Read the scenario, and then answer the following questions.

A Grade 1 teacher has decided to teach his children a lesson on building model chairs out of newspaper. He begins the lesson by asking the children about the kinds of furniture they have seen. One child quickly names all the furniture in her living room at home, but adds that the furniture is too big for her and she would like her favorite chair to have shorter legs so that her feet could touch the ground. Another child adds that he would like to have a chair that has a built in light and a tray on which he could rest his favorite books. A third child adds that he would like a living room chair that automatically became a bed so that he would not have to go to his bedroom at night. A fourth child comments that he wondered who made furniture and whether they would be willing to listen to their ideas.

The teacher then demonstrates how to roll newspapers to make strong columns and how to join newspapers together. One child comments that he thinks he could probably build a chair that could support his father. The other children are skeptical – they think that newspapers are not strong enough to support an adult and even have their doubts whether the chairs will hold them!

The children move into groups and work to share ideas and listen to the suggestions of other children. One child struggles with rolling the newspapers and other children help hold the roll in place as it is being taped together. Another child cannot join columns together – especially where a vertical column meets a horizontal piece. Some children suggest wrapping the horizontal piece around the vertical column while others suggest using more tape.

Finally, the newspaper chairs are assembled. Each group begins to test their chair by sitting on the structures. Some chairs collapse under the load while others support the children. One child states that he should have listened to the suggestions of her group, while another child says that real furniture builders probably have the same problems when they are building.

- What attitudes did the children appear to use as they participated in the building activity?

- How were the attitudes developed by the children's willingness to participate in the activity?

- How would you assist the children to understand that the attitudes used were not unique to a technological problem-solving context?

Textbook Activity 3.6

Looking at the **Alberta Elementary Science Program**

Using your copy of the *Alberta Elementary Science Program* (1996), answer the following questions:

- How do General Learner Expectations (GLEs) relate to Specific Learner Expectations (SLEs)?

- How do Overview paragraphs relate to GLEs and SLEs?

- What are the differences between a concept and a SLE?

- How might an elementary teacher use the conceptual frameworks found in Part D of this Companion Manual?

For the grade level that has been assigned to your group, answer the following questions:

- List the topics and topic emphases for your grade.

- Select one of your grade's topics. Read the topic information (paragraph, GLEs, SLEs). What kinds of knowledge do you still need in order to teach this topic to children?

Chapter 4
Instructional Strategies in STS

Textbook Activity 4.1

What is Teaching?

Consider the following brief scenarios.

- A military leader, with his arm upraised, is giving a speech from a balcony. There is a crowd standing below him, looking upward.

- A man dressed in a suit is standing at a lectern in front of students seated in rows of desks. There is a chalkboard behind him.

- A woman is training a dog to be a guide for the blind. They are outside in a grassy field and the dog is in a harness.

- Two children are seated side by side at a table. There is a small pile of objects on the table and they are placing one object in the pan of a balance.

Now answer the following questions.

- In which of these scenarios is teaching taking place? Why do you think so?

- What else would you need to know to better answer the above question?

Textbook Activity 4.2

Thinking About Teacher Decision-Making and General Pedagogical Strategies

Think about how you would answer the following questions commonly asked by preservice teachers.

- What strategies can be used for organizing group work in science and design technology lessons?

- What strategies can be used to 'grab' children's attention and interest them in the lesson?

- How do you know what teaching strategies to use on a particular day? What influences the selection of a particular strategy?

- How do you know when to intervene to support or direct children and when to stand back?

- What are some appropriate kinds of interventions teachers can use to direct and support children?

- If at the end of the lesson children share a variety of correct and incorrect ideas, what do you do in the subsequent lesson?

- How can you balance a wish to include children's ideas and questions in lessons with the responsibility to teach a mandated curriculum? What criteria can be used to select children's ideas and questions that will become the focus of lessons?

Textbook Activity 4.3

Scientific Inquiry

Current thinking about scientific inquiry suggests that it could be improved by more emphasis on the following five areas (Olson & Loucks-Horsely, 2000):

- Investigating and analyzing science questions rather than demonstrating and verifying science content.

- Using multiple skills to gather evidence in the context of an investigation rather than using individual skills out of context.

- Using evidence and strategies for developing or revising an explanation rather than 'getting an answer'.

- Emphasizing scientific inquiry as argument, explanation, and application where students defend, validate, and apply their conclusions rather than emphasizing scientific inquiry as 'successful' completion of an experiment.

- Having students publicly communicate their ideas, procedures, and explanations to classmates rather than privately to only the teacher.

Now answer the following questions, referring to any scientific inquiry that you have carried out or studied in the context of this course:

- In which of the above five areas did the activity you have selected show the most weakness and what, specifically, were the activity's shortcomings in that area?

- How, specifically, could the inquiry you have selected be changed to show improvement in the area you have criticized (above)?

Textbook Activity 4.4

Teaching About the History and Nature of Science

In 1909, Charles Walcott, secretary of the world-famous Smithsonian Institution, discovered a bed of fossils in British Columbia now known as the Burgess Shale. It is sometimes called the world's most important fossil assemblage because it represents an unprecedented explosion of a huge variety of marine organisms that occurred 550 million years ago. Research the story of the Burgess Shale, then answer the following questions:

- How and why did the discovery of the Burgess Shale change scientists' thinking about life on Earth?

- What theories do scientists put forward as to why this explosion of life took place?

- How could you use the story of the Burgess Shale to teach about the nature of science?

Textbook Activity 4.5

Science and Design Technology Teaching Strategies: Beverley Jane Video

Watch the video entitled *Children Linking Science With Technology*. Then answer the following questions:

- What model of technological problem-solving was suggested by the video (e.g., how did the children start, work through and conclude the project)?
- What comparisons can you make between the Alberta model for technological problem-solving and this example from an Australian classroom?
- What problem-solving skills were practiced by the children?
- What were the children's responsibilities?
- What were the teacher's responsibilities?

Textbook Activity 4.6

Technological Design

Read an actual account of the design of a technological device, building, or consumer product. Review the framework for classroom technological problem-solving described in Chapter 4, then answer the following questions:

- How is each phase of the classroom framework reflected in the account that you read?
- What would you need to add to the framework in terms of teaching interventions so that your design lesson would more authentically reflect professional design?

Textbook Activity 4.7

STS Decision-Making

Read at least three articles about an STS issue that is relevant to the *Alberta Elementary Science Program* (1996) and that would be appropriate for elementary school children. Examples are:

- Should animals be kept in zoos? (Grade 3, Topic E.)
- Should Alberta highways have a special lane reserved only for automobiles that carry more than one person? (Grade 4, Topic C.)
- Should oil drilling be allowed in wetlands? (Grade 5, Topic E.)
- Should space probes be sent to other planets, e.g., the Mars Lander (Grade 6, Topics B and C)?

Review the framework for classroom STS decision-making described in Chapter 4, then answer the following questions:

- How could you use the STS decision-making model in Chapter 4 to plan and teach about your chosen issue?
- How will you ensure that scientific knowledge plays a significant (but not the only) role in the decision-making?
- How will you ensure that children's decisions as to what to do about the issue are based on reasons and evidence?
- What actions do you think would be appropriate for children to take in regards to your chosen issue?

Chapter 5
Planning to Teach STS

Chapter

5

Part A

Textbook Activity 5.1

Planning During Student Teaching

Think of the planning you did during your last student teaching experience. Then answer the following questions:

- What kinds of long-range and short-range science plans did you write?
- What ideas did you take into consideration in order to write good plans?
- What teaching resources proved useful to you? Why were they useful?
- What knowledge would have helped you plan better?
- What advice about planning would you now give to other preservice teachers who are about to begin their student teaching experience?

Textbook Activity 5.2

Balancing Students' Interests With a Mandated Curriculum

Think of the challenge of including students' ideas in your science program. Then answer the following questions.

- Why do many teachers believe students' ideas should be included in their science programs?
- What strategies do teachers use to explore students' interests?
- How can teachers balance students' interests with a mandated program?

Textbook Activity 5.3

Thinking About Conceptual Frameworks and Unit Plans

Think about the general and specific concepts that would comprise a Grade 5 unit on *Electricity and Magnetism*. Use Part D of the Companion Manual to access a conceptual framework for the unit that shows the range of concepts that could be included in the unit and the connections between those concepts. Then answer the following questions:

- How could you use the conceptual framework to construct a unit plan?
- What do you still need to think about in order to teach the unit plan?

Textbook Activity 5.4

Sequencing Lessons

Think about the challenge of deciding how to sequence lessons within a unit plan. Then answer the following questions.

- What factors influence teachers' decision about how to sequence lessons?
- What factors might influence a teacher to diverge from his or her planned sequence?
- How would you relate a teacher's decisions about lesson sequencing to ideas about learning presented in Chapter 2?

Textbook Activity 5.5

Reflecting on Lesson Plans

Teach a science or technology lesson plan to students in an elementary classroom; then answer the following questions:

- How did I manage the learning environment to enhance students' learning?
- How did I monitor and respond to student behavior?
- How did I meet the needs of individual students?
- What were the strongest and weakest aspects of my lesson?
- What ideas about teaching did I gain from teaching this lesson?
- How would I change this lesson the next time I taught it? Why?

Chapter 6
Assessing Children's Learning in STS

Textbook Activity 6.1

Thinking About Assessment Issues

Think about the range of students you encountered during your school years, the kinds of assessment you did, and the purposes to which the assessment was put. Then answer the following questions:

- Would students learn what they were taught if there was no assessment?
- To what extent do you think teaching is assessment–driven?
- In light of ideas about how students' learn, should students be graded before they can achieve proficiency?

Textbook Activity 6.2

Fair and Authentic

Review a copy of one of the Alberta Learning year-end elementary science tests from the exam bank. You can find copies of the tests at this website: **www.exambank.ca** Next, focus on the set of test questions relating to a single topic that you are familiar with, e.g., Animal Life Cycles.

Now answer the following questions, referring to specific test items in your chosen set to support your answer:

- Are the test items fair? Why or why not?
- Are the test items authentic? Why or why not?
- How could one of the items that you are criticizing be improved to make it more fair and authentic?
- Write two new items that you consider to be both fair and authentic that you would add to the test. Explain why they are both fair and authentic.

Textbook Activity 6.3

Formative Assessment

Formative assessment is considered very important in classrooms, however it does pose some practical problems for the teacher. Consider the following three scenarios and answer the questions following each:

Scenario One: *Small groups of students are presenting the procedures and results of their scientific inquiry into the evaporation of water. The first group correctly predicted that the water level in open containers would decrease due to evaporation and that the water level in closed containers would not. They report on how their investigation verified their original predictions. The*

second group made the opposite predictions. They report on how their investigation contradicted their original predictions. The teacher gives Group One a higher grade for their presentation than Group Two.

- What problems do you see with this assessment?
- How can such problems with this kind of assessment be overcome?

Scenario Two: *A teacher walks to a table where a group of four students is engaging in technological problem-solving. She notices that one student, Jenny, is not participating and makes a note of this on her attitude checklist. She then moves to the next table.*

- What problems do you see with this assessment?
- How can such problems with this kind of assessment be overcome?

Scenario Three: *A teacher is holding a classroom discussion about the pros and cons of solar power. Two students, Ellen and Stuart, do most of the talking and make a number of perceptive comments. Several other students say nothing. On a scale of 3 for participation, the teacher gives Ellen and Stuart a 3 and gives the students who say nothing a 0.*

- What problems do you see with this assessment?
- How can such problems with this kind of assessment be overcome?

Textbook Activity 6.4

Strengths and Weaknesses

Consider the following three common methods of assessment: multiple choice tests, portfolios, and performance assessments. Make a chart showing at least four strengths and four weaknesses of each method. Be specific, e.g., if you say that one method is 'subjective', explain why it is subjective.

Now answer the following questions:

- Which of the above three methods do you think is most appropriate for assessing learning? Why?
- How does the above chart support or contradict the claim that teachers should always try to use a variety of assessment methods?

Textbook Activity 6.5

Merit Pay

In some jurisdictions in the United States, systems have been set up whereby teachers are paid bonuses according to how well their students perform on standardized achievement tests (e.g., Denver, Dallas). In some cases, the monetary rewards also go to schools and even to district administrators. Look up two or three articles on 'merit pay' on the World Wide Web and read them.

- Now answer the following questions.
- What are the pros of this policy?
- What are the cons of this policy?
- The underlying assumption of merit pay is that 'teaching (directly) causes learning'. Do you feel this is a valid assumption? Why or why not?

- Would you recommend merit pay be implemented for teachers in the Alberta school system? Why or why not?

Textbook Activity 6.6

Parent-Teacher Meetings

You are a first-year teacher meeting with a parent after having handed out report cards and she tells you that the science grade you gave her child is 'unfair'. She states that her child is an 'A' student whereas the grade you gave is only a 'B'. She wants to know how this happened. Explain how you respond to this parent's concern.

Part B
Sample Activities for Classroom Work

Note:

Completing **all** of the following sample activities will enhance your professional knowledge of scientific inquiry, technological problem-solving, and STS decision-making. Due to time restrictions, however, your course instructor will probably only be able to insert a selection of these activities into the course. Activities not selected should still be read and studied.

The activities have been written using a variety of formats in order to model different teaching strategies. Some activities are quite prescriptive and provide step-by-step instruction. Other activities are more open-ended and allow for a variety of solutions. Should you choose to use some of these activities with children, you still need to modify the activities and use one of the lesson plan formats shown in the main textbook. Most important to add to your lesson plans would be a precise summary of the concepts, skills, and attitudes the children would work towards in the lesson and ideas about how you would assess the children's learning.

Before doing similar activities with children, you should always consider the following safety issues:

- **Safety.** Be cognizant of and follow recognized safety rules and procedures

- Allergies. Are any of the children allergic to any foods or other substances they might be handling or otherwise coming in contact with (e.g., latex, various plants or animals, chemicals, etc.)?

- **Eye and skin safety.** Will the children be working with materials or objects that could be dangerous or irritating to their eyes or skin? Will the children be working with materials that could cause infections (e.g., soil and pond water bacteria and viruses)?

- **General behavioral safety.** Are the children aware of and responsible about general safety guidelines for doing in-class experiments and investigations (e.g., handling glass, liquids, and sharp or pointy objects; being calm and orderly, etc.)? Are children aware of and responsible about conducting themselves safely during out-of-class activities (e.g., field trips, crossing streets, etc.)?

Scientific Inquiry Activities

Scientific Inquiry Activities

Part B

Activity 1
Ice Cube Activities – Thinking About Fair Tests

Background Information: This activity is intended to help children develop a basic understanding of melting, freezing, heat transfer, and temperature and fits well with the *Alberta Elementary Science Program* (1996) topics *Exploring Liquids* (Grade 2), *Seasonal Changes* (Grade 1), *Hot and Cold Temperature* (Grade 2), *Buoyancy and Boats* (Grade 2), *Weather Watch* (Grade 5), and *Classroom Chemistry* (Grade 5).

Some concepts that could be explored through ice cube investigations include:

- Air contains water vapor.
- In general, a substance can be classified as a solid or a liquid or a gas.
- The processes of melting, freezing, evaporating, and condensing do not change what a substance is made.
- Energy, often in the form of heat, is required for melting and evaporation to take place.

During this class, you will have the opportunity to explore a number of questions that have been asked by children who have participated in ice cube activities and to experience what is involved in designing a fair test.

Ice Cubes Activities – Thinking About Fair Tests

Part A: Children's Questions About Ice Cubes

1. Will ice melt faster in water or in air if both are at the same temperature?
2. Does stirring ice in water affect the melting speed? Does it matter how fast the water is stirred? (do NOT stir with a thermometer)
3. Does the amount of water affect the melting time?
4. Does the temperature of the water affect the melting time?

Activity:

5. Select one question from the above list and work to solve the problem (you should have time to investigate all four questions). Complete the following as you work through your fair tests.
6. Question:

7. Expectation of Activity Outcome; What Influenced You To Have This Expectation?
8. How will you make this a fair test?
9. List and identify the variables involved in solving this question.
10. Results: (Graphs? Charts?)
11. Tentative answer to your initial question (hypothesis).
12. Testable questions you now want to explore.
13. Select a second question from the list and again work through the steps listed above

Part B: Child's Question About Adding Salt to Ice

What happens to ice temperature when salt is added to ice?

Activity:

Think about how you might use the materials available to you to go about answering this question. Conduct a fair test that will help you gain some insight into the phenomenon of adding salt to ice. Make sure that you allow plenty of time for the ice to interact with the salt. Record your tentative answer to the ice and salt question. What is your best explanation for what you observed?

Part C: Scenarios and Questions

- Linda said that ice will float only if the water is deeper than the ice; if the water is shallow, the ice won't float.

  John said, "Ice will float if there is as much water as there is ice."

  - Do you agree with Linda? ... with John? ... with neither of them?
  - If you think they're both wrong, can you prove that they are wrong?

- Jose asked his mother if he could borrow her electric fan. He wanted to see if he could keep an ice cube for a long time by putting it in front of the fan, since he used a fan to keep cool in summer. His mother said he could use a fan, but she thought the ice would melt faster in front of it because she used a fan to defrost her refrigerator more quickly. What do you think Jose found when he tried his experiment? How can you explain this?

Part D: Thinking About Everyday Life

1. You have frozen water pipes in your RV – what should you do?

2. Your frozen slush drink is too frozen to get through the straw to your mouth – what can you do?

3. A child has her tongue stuck to a cold metal fence – what should you do?

4. Why does southern Ontario use more salt on their highways than Alberta?

Part E: Post-Activity Discussion

1. Presentation of results. Identification of variables.

2. What factors speed up the melting rate? What do these factors have in common?

References

Couchman, J. K., MacBean, J. C., Stecher, A., & Wentworth, D. F. (1976). *Snow and Ice (Examining Your Environment)*. ON: Holt, Rinehart, & Winston.

Elementary Science Study. (1974). *Ice Cubes: Melting rates of Ice*. NY: Webster

Activity 2

Mealworm Activities –Thinking About Working With Living Things

Background Information: Activities with mealworms are intended to help children develop a basic understanding of an animal's life cycle, the characteristics of this animal, and its adaptation to different environments. Mealworm activities fit well with the *Alberta Elementary Science Program* (1996) topics *Animal Life Cycles* (Grade 3) and *Small Crawling and Flying Animals* (Grade 2).

Mealworms are the larva stage of the darkling beetle (Tenebrio molitor). The darkling beetle is an example of an insect that undergoes a complete metamorphosis (all 4 stages). The egg stage lasts 1-2 weeks and is followed by a 4-6 month larval stage. The larva changes into pupae (1-3 weeks) which, in turn, becomes an adult (1 month).

Mealworms can be used to help children construct an understanding of these, and other, concepts:

- Animals have features which enable them to meet their needs.

- Animals have parts which enable them to meet their needs.

- Animals respond to changes in their environment.

- Each kind of animal continues because offspring of the same kind are produced.

- Each kind of animal produces enough young to ensure the continued existence of its kind.

- Animals go through a sequence of changes from young to adult to young; this is called a life cycle.

- Plants and animals depend on other plants and animals.

- Different kinds of plant and animal populations exist in various environments.

- Plants and animals are affected by the nonliving features of their environment.

- The size of plant and animal populations are interdependent, because of food needs.

- Animals exhibit great diversity and can be grouped according to visible characteristics.

During this class you will have the opportunity to explore one or more questions that have been asked by children who have participated in a mealworm activities.

Mealworm Activities – Thinking About Working With Living Things

Children's Questions About Mealworms:

1. Do mealworms prefer a certain color?

2. What is the steepest incline mealworms can climb?

3. On what kinds of surfaces can mealworms walk?

4. How fast do mealworms move? How fast can the fastest mealworm go?

Observational Study:

5. Begin by spending a short time observing a mealworm with a hand lens. Draw a picture of your mealworm. Can you label any parts?

Experimental Studies:

6. Select one question from the above list and work with a partner to solve the problem (you should have time for all four questions). Complete the following as you work through your fair tests.

7. Question:

8. Prediction (involves forecasting a future event based on a previously developed understanding):

9. How will you make this a fair test?

10. List and identify the variables involved in solving this question:

11. Results: (Graphs? Charts?)

12. Your explanation of events:

13. Testable questions you now want to explore:

14. Select a second question from the list and again work through the steps listed above.

Post-Activity Discussion:

1. For each of the four questions, what variables did you identify? What did you have to do in order to lend more validity and reliability to your results? What did you find out?

2. What do your results suggest about:
   - where mealworms might prefer to live?
   - how mealworms might hide from danger?
   - how mealworms might get into your house?

References

Elementary Science Study. (1976). *Behavior of mealworms*. NY: McGraw-Hill.

Kramer, D.C. (1985). The classroom animal: Mealworms. *Science and Children*, 22 (4), 25-26.

McGlathery, G. (1989). Mealworms in the classroom. *Science and Children*, 26 (6), 29-31.

Activity 3

Ball and Funnel - Thinking About the Goals of Science Teaching

Background Information: The ball and funnel activity relates to the *Alberta Elementary Science Program* (1996) topics *Flight* (Grade 6) and *Air and Aerodynamics*

(Grade 6). It provides a good opportunity for students to think about some of the overall goals for teaching science (e.g., concepts, skills, attitudes, nature of science, everyday applications, and STS). The key science idea underlying the activity is Bernoulli's Principle.

Bernoulli's Principle, named after Swiss scientist Daniel Bernoulli, states that increased fluid velocity produces decreased pressure. Within the same fluid (e.g., air), high-speed flow is associated with low pressure, and low-speed flow is associated with high pressure.

Bernoulli's Principle helps explain the lift produced by an airplane wing. The wing is designed so that is curved on top. As the airplane moves through the air forward, the air moves more rapidly over the upper surface of the wing than its lower surface, thereby decreasing pressure above the wing. At the same time, the air flowing more slowly on the lower surface of the wing increases the pressure below the wing. The difference between the decreased pressure above the wing and the increased pressure below produces the force of lift. A wing with more curvature on the top surface has greater lift than a wing with flat surfaces.

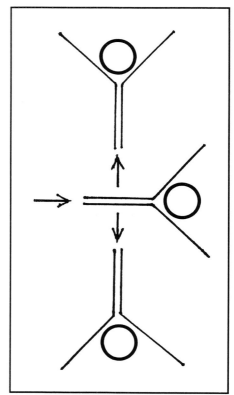

Figure B1

Ball and Funnel Activity

For this activity you need a funnel with a narrow stem and a ping pong ball that fits inside the mouth of the funnel. You are to place the ball in the funnel and, holding the funnel in three different positions, blow into the stem of the funnel and see what happens to the ball (See Figure B1). Then you will try to explain what happened. When you explain you must remember that your explanation must "fit the facts" (i.e., your explanation must account for and not contradict what you observed).

Predicting, Observing, and Explaining:

Hold the funnel vertically with its mouth pointing upward toward the ceiling and place the ball in the funnel.

- What do you think will happen to the ball when you blow into the stem of the funnel? Why?

Blow smoothly and strongly into the stem and observe the behavior of the ball. Try blowing harder and softer.

- What do you observe?
- How do you explain what you observe?
- How could you test your explanation?

Hold the funnel with its mouth pointing horizontally and place the ball in the funnel. You will need to hold the ball snugly into the funnel until you have started blowing.

- What do you think will happen to the ball when you blow into the stem of the funnel? Why?

Hold the ball in the funnel with one finger, blow smoothly and strongly into the stem, and take your finger off the ball. Observe the behavior of the ball. Try blowing harder and softer.

- What do you observe?
- How do you explain what you observe?
- How could you test your explanation?

Hold the funnel with its mouth pointing toward the floor and place the ball in the funnel. Again, you will need to hold the ball snugly into the funnel until you have started blowing. It is suggested you stand up when you blow into the funnel.

- What do you think will happen to the ball when you blow into the stem of the funnel? Why?

Hold the ball in the funnel with one finger, blow smoothly and strongly into the stem, and take your finger off the ball. Observe the behavior of the ball. Try blowing harder and softer.

- What do you observe?
- How do you explain what you observe?
- How could you test your explanation?

Discrepant Events:

- How would you describe your reaction to what you observed when you placed the ball in the funnel and blew into the funnel?
- How would evoking this kind of reaction help you teach science to your students?

A *discrepant event* is a science activity or experiment that has a surprising result. The discrepancy is between what you expect and what actually happens.

Goals of Science Teaching:

- What concepts did you learn?
- What skills did you use to conduct this inquiry?
- What attitudes do you think are associated with doing scientific inquiry?
- What did you learn about the nature of science?
- How does what you found out help explain how the shape of an airplane wing makes it possible for the airplane to fly?
- A positive aspect of airplanes is that they can help us get quickly to faraway places. What are some negative aspects of airplanes?

Reference

Liem, Tik (1989). *Invitations to Science Inquiry.* California: Science Inquiry Enterprises.

Related Website

http://www.scienceinquiry.com

Activity 4

Beaks and Food – Interpreting Data

Background Information: This activity can help to develop an understanding of bird adaptations, specifically beak type. It fits well with the Grade 3 topic *Animal Life Cycles* and can help children understand how adaptations allow animals to thrive in different environments.

Adaptations can be structural (e.g., beak shape), behavioral (how the beak is used), or physiological. Adaptations allow members of a species (e.g., ospreys) to compete successfully with members of their own species and members of other species (e.g., eagles), and to survive their physical environment.

Certain individuals of a species are better able to survive and reproduce than others are because they possess traits that are useful in the struggle for existence. These traits may be shared by or partially shared by other individuals of their population. Not every trait of an individual or of a species is optimally adapted. Since the individual as a whole is the target of selection, many neutral or even slightly harmful genes may be carried in a population along with favorable gene combinations.

Adaptations are, on the whole, the result of natural selection. Natural selection occurs in natural populations or populations where breeding is not controlled by people. Natural selection occurs as follows:

• Natural populations vary. Variations are produced primarily through mutation and secondarily through recombination of genes via sexual reproduction.

• Variations are tested in the environment. Some offspring survive and reproduce and others die. (In most natural populations, parents produce far more offspring than nature can tolerate.)

• The adaptation that has survival value (e.g., body color of tadpoles that allows them to hide, or the ability of orchid seeds to survive long periods of dry weather) is most likely to be preserved in any offspring. In turn, the survivor will pass on the genes for this adaptation to some of their offspring. Then the adaptation is tested again.

Beaks and Food Activity

Activity Purpose: This activity investigates which structural adaptations in birds, specifically beak type, help birds better obtain food. It is also an example of an **inductive** approach to science teaching. An inductive approach begins from many examples to draw general conclusions about all the examples.

Beak and Food Station Materials: Pin, spoon, scissors, tweezers, wood splint, and tongs.

Food Station	Food in Containe	Stomach
1.	Foam chips in aquarium water	Beaker/measuring cup
2.	Raw macaroni on tray	Beaker/measuring cup
3.	Cereal in sand on tray	Beaker/measuring cup
4.	Seeds on tray	Beaker/measuring cup
5.	Marbles in round bowl	Plastic beaker/ measuring cup
6.	Elastics on tray	Beaker/measuring cup

Predictions: Based on your initial observations of the beaks and food, predict which beak type you think will do the best job of picking up each different kind of food. Also, predict which beak type will obtain the most food overall. Explain the reasoning behind each of your predictions.

Food	Best Beak	Why?
Foam chips		
Raw macaroni		
Cereal		
Seeds		
Marbles		
Elastics		

Procedure: Each individual selects a beak type. Form groups of the same size such that all different beak types are represented once in the group. At each station, each group member, in turn, uses his or her beak to get as much of each different food type into the 'stomach' (beaker) as possible in 15 seconds. Other group members can judge if the beak is used 'properly'. Return the food to its container each time.

Observations: Record the volume of stomach contents for each type of food. Use the appropriate beaker to measure the volume in millilitres (not number of pieces) so you have a common unit to compare across food types.

Your Beak Type _____

Food Volumes Eaten By Your Beak:

Food	Volume
Foam chips	
Raw macaroni	
Cereal	
Seeds	
Marbles	
Elastics	

Data Collection (Totals of All Beaks, All Foods):

When you have completed all the food stations, meet with students from other groups who have the same beak type as you (e.g., all spoon bills meet together). Total the volume of all your stomachs together for each food eaten and record the totals in the appropriate row and columns of the chart at the bottom of the page.

Interpreting The Data:

Look for patterns in your data and think about what they mean in terms of beak type and food. Then answer the questions that follow.

Relationships:

- Which beak type worked best/worst with each different kind of food?
- Which beak type obtained the most/least food over all?
- Were your original predictions accurate or not? Why?

Generalizations:

- What generalizations can we make about beaks and food?

Explanations:

- Why do particular birds eat particular foods?
- What is adaptation?
- How do we explain adaptation?
- What is the theory of natural selection?
- Can we "discover" natural selection from our activity? Why or why not?

Reflections:

- What does the activity imply about teaching?
- What does the activity imply about learning?
- What else did you learn from this activity?

Related Website

As a follow-up, read about the present-day research on Darwin's finches by Peter and Rosemary Grant. **http://www.pbs.org/wgbh/evolution/library/01/6/l_016_01.html**

Data Chart: Total Food Eaten By All Beaks

	Pin	Spoon	Scissors	Tweezers	Wood Splint	Tongs	Total
Foam Chips							
Raw Mac							
Cheerios							
Seeds							
Marbles							
Elastics							
Totals							

Activity 5

Sticky Water-Thinking About Science Teaching

Background Information: The activity fits well with the *Alberta Elementary Science Program* (1996) topic *Exploring Liquids* (Grade 2). The activity would need to be modified for children because it is deliberately designed to challenge the thinking of preservice teachers to help them get a sense of how children might take up this kind of intellectual challenge. The activity provides a good opportunity to think about how science can be taught authentically yet still be accessible to students.

Cohesion and Viscosity

Liquids do not maintain a shape because the molecules slide easily by one another, so a liquid takes the shape of its container. Water (H_2O) has more structure than many other liquids. When water molecules are close together, their positive and negative regions are attracted to the oppositely-charged regions of other molecules. The force of attraction is called a hydrogen bond (H–O). Each water molecule is hydrogen bonded to four other water molecules. The continual making and breaking of hydrogen bonds in water provides a weak force called *cohesion* which holds the molecules together.

Cohesion is the cause of viscosity, which refers to the 'thickness' of the liquid. Salad oil is more viscous than water, and honey is more viscous than salad oil. Liquids with a higher viscosity flow more slowly than liquids with a lower viscosity.

Laminar and Turbulent Flow

If you turn on a faucet, you will see glassy, orderly flow called *laminar* flow. If there is no disturbance, smooth flow continues. In laminar flow, fluid particles move along straight, parallel paths in layers (laminar). The viscosity of the fluid dominates and suppresses any tendency to disturb the smooth flow. If you turn on the faucet a little more, water close to the faucet still flows slowly and smoothly in laminar flow. But as the water falls, it speeds up due to the force of gravity. Farther down, the flow of the water becomes rough and convoluted in what is called *turbulent* flow. In turbulent flow, the particles of the fluid move haphazardly in all directions.

When the faucet is turned to full on, the entire stream is in turbulent flow with the flow pattern changing all the time. Although the average motion is downward, within the flow there are irregularities everywhere. The movement of the water is chaotic and involves extensive mixing of water and air.

Factors Affecting Flow: Speed, Diameter, and Viscosity

Various factors affect whether flow will be laminar or turbulent. As we have seen, speed is one factor. Slow fluid flow tends to be laminar. As it speeds up, a transition occurs into complicated, random turbulent flow.

Diameter also affects flow. An even, slow flow coming from a large diameter tap can be turbulent. If you put a nozzle on your tap and constrict the water flow into a fine tube, it can go quite fast without becoming turbulent.

If you replace the water in your pipes with honey, even for fast flow the motion would remain laminar. Honey has a higher viscosity than water and the viscosity resists transition to turbulence. At a speed of flow where water is turbulent the honey can remain laminar.

Laminar flow then, occurs for low speeds, small diameters, and high viscosity, while turbulent flows occur for the opposite conditions–high speeds, large diameters, and low viscosity.

Drops of Falling Water

We have already noted that the falling stream of water from a faucet speeds up due to gravity. The increase in speed is a key factor causing the downward flow to change from laminar to turbulent.

Air resistance is another reason the falling water breaks up. When a stream of water falls through the air, air resistance disturbs and deforms the shape of the stream. This helps the cohesion of the water to break up the stream into droplets. A drop of water tends to assume the shape of a sphere due to the force of cohesion.

Why don't the falling drops recombine to make a single stream again? The main reason is that they are falling together downwards, not sideways. So since nothing causes them to meet each other while falling they can't come together to form a single stream.

Sticky Water

Materials:

Medicine cups, eye droppers, containers for water, two streaming bottles, masking tape, water, dish soap.

Advance Preparation:

Make up a concentrated solution of dish soap and water. Let the solution stand for at least an hour, stirring occasionally.

Heaping Water:

Fill a small medicine cup with as much plain water as possible. Use an eye dropper to assist you to get it full.

- What criterion could you use to judge that the cup is 'full'?
- What do you observe about the full cup?
- How do you explain what you observe?

Falling Water:

Turn on a faucet slightly so that a stream of water forms. Adjust the tap so that the stream begins as smooth, then breaks into droplets before it reaches the sink. You can also try pouring water from one container to another to achieve the same effect.

- How could you relate the change in the appearance of the falling water to your explanation for what you observed about the full medicine cup?

Streaming Water:

Obtain two streaming bottles. If necessary, make streaming bottles out of empty plastic bottles with metal lids, for example, from hair gel. Make a small hole in the lid using a nail. Make another slightly larger hole in the bottom of the bottle.

Fill one streaming bottle with plain water and put on the lid. Turn the bottle upside down, keeping your finger covering the hole in the bottom. Uncover the hole and let the water stream fall into the sink. Have someone else use a roll of masking tape to measure the distance from the mouth of the bottle to where the smooth stream breaks up into droplets. Tear off a length of tape that matches the length of the smooth stream and display it.

Fill the other streaming bottle with soapy water and repeat the procedure. Compare the second length of tape to the first one.

- If there is a difference in the lengths of the two pieces of tape, how do you explain it?

Heaping Soapy Water:

Fill one medicine cup with plain water as you did in the first activity and another medicine cup with soapy water. Compare the two results.

- What do you observe?
- How do you explain what you observe?
- What do your findings tell you about the respective properties of the smooth and droplet parts of the flow of tap water?

Cohesion:

Find out about the property of water known as *cohesion*. Explain the following phenomena, using what you find out.

- The medicine cup filled with plain water.
- The change in the appearance of the stream of tap water.
- The difference between the stream of plain water and the stream of soapy water.
- The difference between the medicine cup filled with plain water and the medicine cup filled with soapy water.

What Counts as Science Teaching?:

Discuss whether the teaching of this science activity had any of the following features (Munby and Roberts, 1998):

- Did both instructor and students provide evidence to support their claims?
- Did both instructor and students provide logical arguments to support their claims?
- Were discrepancies in observations resolved through reasoning based on evidence?
- Were opportunities given to discuss the plausibility and grounds for explanations?
- Were alternative explanations respected?
- Were the criteria made clear for choosing between alternative explanations?
- Were student ideas, questions, and objections honored and treated with regard to reasons?
- Were reasons given if claims were called into question?

References

Elementary Science Study (1976). *Kitchen Physics*. NY: McGraw Hill.

Munby, H.,& Roberts, D. A. (1998). Intellectual independence: A potential link between science teaching and responsible citizenship. In D. A. Roberts & L. Ostman (Eds.), *Problems of Meaning in Curriculum* (pp. 101-114). New York: Teachers College Press.

Activity 6

Disappearing Volume – Thinking About the Nature of Science

Background Information: The two overall goals of this set of activities are to teach about solutions and, simultaneously, about the nature of scientific explanations (theories). The activity fits well with the *Alberta Elementary Science Program* (1996) topic *Classroom Chemistry* (Grade 5).

Solutions and Molecules

All matter that is not a single substance is made up of invisible particles called molecules. The molecules of a substance have spaces between them. For example, in any volume of water there are spaces between the water molecules that make up the water.

When two liquids are mixed together to create a solution, the molecules of the two liquids intermingle and disperse among each other. In fact, a solution is defined as a homogenous mixture of two or more substances. If the two liquids are different, their molecules will be of different sizes. For example, when you mix water and methyl alcohol, there are spaces between the water molecules. When the alcohol mingles with the water, the empty spaces between the water molecules get 'filled' by alcohol molecules. This reduces the total final volume of the water-alcohol solution.

The same principle can apply to mixing liquids and solids. Certain molecules (e.g., ordinary table salt or sodium chloride, NaCl) are formed by naturally charged positive and negative particles called ions (e.g., $Na+$ and $Cl-$), held together by their electric attraction to each other. These molecules may fall apart when dissolved in water. For example, table salt or sodium chloride separates into $Na+$ and $Cl-$ when dissolved in water. The tiny ions can fit between the water molecules, again reducing the total volume of the water-salt solution.

Teacher Note: You must measure all volumes very carefully and ensure that the 50 ml graduated cylinders are completely clean and dry before liquid is poured into them. Add 50 ml to 50 ml for more dramatic results.

Safety Warning: Methyl alcohol is poisonous. You should do some of these activities with children as demonstrations.

Disappearing Volume: Thinking About the Nature of Science

Activity 1: Water and Water
Materials:

Water, two 25 ml graduated cylinders, one 50 ml graduated cylinder, 40 ml beaker, medicine dropper, two small funnels, and a stirring rod.

Predict: What will be the total volume when 25 ml water is added to 25 ml water?

Procedure:

• Carefully measure exactly 25 ml of water in one 25 ml graduated cylinder and exactly 25 ml water in the other 25 ml graduated cylinder (use a medicine dropper for precision). Combine the two volumes in a clean, dry 50 ml graduated cylinder. Stir the mixture and let it stand for 1 minute.

• **Observe** and record the total volume.

• **Explain** why the total volume is what it is.

Activity 2: Alcohol and Alcohol
Materials:

Methyl alcohol, two 25 ml graduated cylinders, one 50 ml graduated cylinder, 40 ml beaker, medicine dropper, two small funnels, and a stirring rod.

Predict: What will be the total volume when 25 ml alcohol is added to 25 ml alcohol?

Procedure:

• Carefully measure exactly 25 ml of alcohol in one 25 ml graduated cylinder and exactly 25 ml alcohol in the other 25 ml graduated cylinder (use a medicine dropper for precision). Combine the two volumes in a clean, dry 50 ml graduated cylinder. Stir the mixture and let it stand for 1 minute. (Note: Save the alcohol for future use.)

- **Observe** and record the total volume.
- **Explain** why the total volume is what it is.
- How does your explanation also account for what you observed in Activity 1?

Activity 3: Water and Alcohol
Materials:

Methyl alcohol, water, two 25 ml graduated cylinders, one 50 ml graduated cylinder, 40 ml beaker, two medicine droppers, two small funnels, and a stirring rod.

Predict: What will be the total volume when 25 ml alcohol is added to 25 ml water?

Procedure:

- Carefully measure exactly 25 ml of alcohol in one 25 ml graduated cylinder and exactly 25 ml water in the other 25 ml graduated cylinder (use a medicine dropper for precision). Combine the two volumes in a clean, dry 50 ml graduated cylinder. Stir the mixture and let it stand for 1 minute.
- **Observe** and record the total volume.
- **Explain** why the total volume is what it is.
- How does your explanation also account for what you observed in the two previous activities?

Activity 4: Liquid and Solid (Regular Salt)
Materials:

Salt, warm water, 40 ml beaker, 140 ml beaker, large beaker, medicine dropper, and a spoon.

Predict: How far will the water level rise if you add 40 ml of salt?

Procedure:

- Fill the 140 ml beaker to the 100 ml mark with warm water (use the medicine dropper to be precise).
- Slowly add the 40 ml salt to the water. Stir the mixture and let it stand for 1 minute.
- **Observe** the water level.
- How does any change in the water level compare with the amount of salt you added: The same? More? Less?
- **Explain** the observed result.
- How does your explanation also account for what you observed in the three previous activities?

Activity 5: Liquid and Solid (Salt Pellets)
Materials:

Salt pellets for a water softener, warm water, 500 ml Florence (round) flask, rubber stopper, and an erasable felt pen.

Predict: What will happen to the water level if you let the flask stand for one minute?

Procedure:

- Fill the round part of the flask about 1/4 with salt pellets. Add warm water until the liquid level is about halfway up the narrow neck of the flask. Quickly stopper the flask. Mark the liquid level on the neck of the flask with a felt pen.
- **Observe** the liquid level again after letting the flask stand for one minute.
- **Explain** the observed result.
- How does your explanation also account for what you observed in the four previous activities?

Activity 6: Liquid and Solid (Sugar)
Materials:

Sugar, warm water, 40 ml beaker, 140 ml beaker, large beaker, medicine dropper, and a spoon.

Predict: How far will the water level rise if you add 40 ml of sugar?

Procedure:

- Fill the 140 ml beaker to the 100 ml mark with warm water (use the medicine dropper to be precise).
- Carefully add 40 ml sugar of sugar to the water. Stir the mixture and let it stand for 1 minute.
- **Observe** the water level.
- How does any change in the water level compare with the amount of sugar you added: The same? More? Less?
- **Explain** the observed result.
- How does your explanation also account for what you observed in the five previous activities?

Thinking About the Nature of Scientific Explanations:

Discuss whether this set of activities illustrates any of the following features of a scientific explanation:

- Answers the question "Why"?

- Proposes a cause (or causes) for a phenomena or event, or for a set of phenomena or events.

- Accounts for patterns in what is observed.

- Explains phenomena and events in terms of 'postulated' entities such as molecules and genes.

- Explains at a level where events are invisible (cannot be directly observed).

Activity 7

Laws of Magnetism

Background Information: This activity fits well with the *Alberta Elementary Science Program* (1996) topics *Magnetism* (Grade 2) and *Electricity and Magnetism* (Grade 5). It is a good opportunity to clarify the difference between scientific laws and scientific theories.

The Laws of Magnetism are:

- Like poles repel.

- Unlike poles attract.

The Laws of Magnetism are generalizations about ALL magnets. The laws incorporate observations about what magnetic poles 'do' to each other – repel or attract, and inferences about the relationship between the two poles – poles can be like and unlike. The relationships are derived from observations of what two poles do to the same third pole, i.e., attract or repel.

Laws of Magnetism

Preparations:

- Select two long bar magnets (you will also need a third magnet later).

- Wrap tape around the ends of each magnet to cover the N or S that indicates the pole.

- Label the ends of one magnet A and B.

- Label the ends of the other magnet C and D (note: label the C-D magnet so that A attracts D is true; then all classroom groups will get the same results).

- Tie a 15 cm piece of string around the middle of the A-B magnet so it can swing freely.

Observations:

Dangle the A-B magnet from the string so it is approximately parallel to the table. Try slowly bringing each of the poles of the C-D magnet near each of the poles of the A-B magnet, in turn. Keep track of your observations by writing them in terms of "attracts" or "repels":

A _____ C   B _____ C

A _____ D   B _____ D

Relationships (Unlike):

What 'unlike' relationships can you infer from your four observations? (Note: Keep in mind that the relationships also work in reverse, e.g., A attracts D also means D attracts A.) That is, do your observations of the behavior of the magnets suggest anything about the unlikeness of any of the poles? (Hint: Do any two poles do something different [attract or repel] when brought near the same third pole?) Write down any relationships you can infer in the form of "A is unlike B because ..."

- When you can infer nothing more about the relationships among the poles of the magnets, what should you do in order to find out more?

More Preparations:

- Wrap tape around the ends of your third magnet to cover the N or S that indicates the pole.

- Label the ends of the magnet E and F (note: label the E-F magnet so that A attracts E is true; then all classroom groups will get the same results).

More Observations:

- Dangle the A-B magnet from the string again. Bring each of the poles of the E-F magnet near each of the poles of the A-B magnet, in turn. Record your observations.

- Remove the string from the A-B magnet and use it to dangle the C-D magnet. Bring each of the poles of the E-F magnet near each of the poles of the C-D magnet, in turn. Record your observations.

- Finally, copy your four observations from the previous "Observations" section to put all your observations together.

A _____ E   C _____ E   A _____ C

A _____ F   C _____ F   A _____ D

B _____ E   D _____ E   B _____ C

B _____ F   D _____ F   B _____ D

More Relationships: Like and Unlike

What 'like' relationships can you infer from your twelve observations? What new unlike relationships can you infer? Write any additional relationships you infer in the form of "X is like Y because …"

Classifying the Poles:

Divide your six magnetic poles into two groups of three so that within each of the two groups, all three poles are like each other and unlike all the members of the other group.

Group 1:

Group 2:

Generalizing:

Try logically deriving the two Laws of Magnetism by combining your observations (attract/repel) with your inferred relationships (like/unlike) into two generalizations about all magnets. Knowing the laws already will assist you with your reasoning. However, you must derive the laws from your reasoning rather than assume the validity of the laws as the basis for your reasoning (i.e., you cannot say, "Because like poles repel and unlike poles attract, I know that …").

• Verbally explain your reasoning to someone else.

Testing Your Generalizations:

• How could you test your generalizations to show that they accurately describe the behavior of magnets?

• How can you use prediction as part of your testing?

Thinking About the Laws of Magnetism:

• How do scientists explain the Laws of Magnetism (i.e., explain why magnets attract and repel)?

• What evidence supports the Theory of Magnetism?

• What is the difference between a theory and a law?

Related Information: Fluid Theory, Molecular Theory, and Magnetic Domains

Nineteenth century scientists believed that magnetism was caused by the behavior of invisible magnetic fluids.

They believed there were two kinds of magnetic fluids surrounding the molecules of the magnet, each fluid repelling its own kind and attracting the other kind. A material was magnetized when the fluids were separated and driven to opposite ends of the material. The difference of the two poles arose from the nature of the fluids predominating in them: poles containing the same kind of fluid repelled while those containing opposite kinds attracted. The fluid theory was discarded as it could not explain many observations concerning magnetism.

More recently, scientists decided that magnetism in a magnetic material was due to the nature and arrangement of the molecules inside the material. They believed that every molecule in a magnetic material behaved like a tiny magnet, with a north-seeking and a south-seeking pole. When the magnetic material was not magnetized, the molecules were arranged in a haphazard way so that the poles neutralized (or acted against) each other. But, when the magnetic material was magnetized, all the molecules lined up so that all north-seeking poles were facing one direction and all south-seeking poles were facing the opposite direction. This arrangement left free north-seeking poles at one end of the magnet and free south-seeking poles at the other end.

The molecular theory explained why the force of the magnets was strongest at the ends (where there were free poles of one kind) and weakest in the middle (where north and south poles were together). The theory also explained why a magnetized bar, when cut in half, produced two new magnets even though the middle of the magnetized bar originally had little magnetism compared to the poles.

Currently, scientists theorize that the magnetism of magnetic materials is due to the spinning movement of the electrons as they revolve or travel around the nucleus of the atom. Each spinning electron acts as a tiny magnet. In atoms of non-magnetic materials half their electrons spin in one direction and half spin in the opposite direction, canceling their magnetic effects. In atoms of magnetized materials more electrons spin in one direction than the other, making each atom a tiny magnet. The more electrons an atom has spinning in one direction than in the other direction, the |more strongly magnetic the material will be. The magnetized atoms group together in large clusters called domains, which line up like the molecules in the molecular theory do.

The theory of magnetic domains explains why iron (and cobalt and nickel) is a strongly magnetic material. An iron atom has 26 electrons. There are 2 electrons in the first shell, 8 electrons in the second shell, 14 electrons in the third shell, and 2 electrons in the fourth (outer) shell. Scientists think that in the first, second, and fourth shells there are just as many electrons spinning in one direction as in the other direction. But in the third shell there are 9 electrons spinning in one direction and 5 spinning in the opposite direction. This means there are four electrons that are not canceling each other out. That is why iron is strongly magnetic.

It should be noted that iron, cobalt, and nickel, the three magnetic metals, are beside each other in the Periodic Table (i.e., atomic numbers 26, 27, and 28). This proximity supports the idea that magnetism and atomic structure are linked.

References

This activity is based on the teaching of Dr. Douglas A. Roberts, Professor Emeritus, University of Calgary. Dr. Roberts is an internationally known award-winning science educator, who has been instrumental in the schooling of many science educators now teaching in universities in Canada and elsewhere. He has played an important role in the development of science textbook series now used in Alberta junior high and high schools and elsewhere in Canada.

Activity 8

Electrical Circuits

Background: The design of this activity is based on constructivist ideas about learning applied to teaching about electricity, in particular, as set out in the writings of Osborne and Freyberg (1984). The activity fits well with the *Alberta Elementary Science Program* (1996) topics *Electricity and Magnetism* (Grade 5) and *Mechanisms Using Electricity* (Grade 5).

The activity focuses on three key ideas about electricity:

• A simple electrical circuit is made up of a source of electricity (e.g., a battery), a path along which the current can travel (e.g., copper wire), and an appliance that uses electricity (e.g., a bulb).

• Electricity flows from the source at the negative end along the path through the appliance and returns through a second path to the source at the positive end (one-way, return).

• The "amount" of electrical current is the same in all parts of the circuit (nothing is used up).

Electrical Current

All matter consists of tiny atoms. Atoms are made up of three tinier particles–protons, neutrons, and electrons. Electrons are outside the nucleus or centre of the atom. Each electron is negatively charged.

When an electrical current flows through a material electrons move from atom to atom of the material. How easily the electrons move depends on how tightly the atoms of the material hold onto their electrons. A material that holds loosely to its electrons is called a *conductor*.

An electrical current is the *flow of electrical charge*, measured in amperes or amps. In a solid conductor (e.g., copper wire), electrons carry the charge through the circuit. (Note: This is tricky; electrons carry the charge but they are not the charge.) Charges flow when there is a difference in electric potential (i.e., difference in voltage) across the ends of a conductor. The flow continues until the potential is equal at both ends. A voltage source provides a potential difference by acting as a 'voltage pump'. A good source maintains a steady flow of charge.

A battery is an example of a voltage source. In a battery, energy released by a chemical reaction occurring inside the battery is changed into electrical energy. The energy is available at the battery terminals. When the battery is connected into an electrical circuit, the electrical energy (charge) flows through the circuit.

Electrical Units

An ampere or amp is the unit of electric current flowing in a circuit. A house circuit is about 15-20 amps. A volt is the unit of electric potential in the power source. A flashlight battery is 1.5 volts. A standard house circuit is 110 volts but some house appliances, (e.g., stove, dryer) are on a circuit of 220 volts.

Electrical Current in a Simple Circuit – A Constructivist View

Introduction:

The electric circuit activity builds on three basic principles:

- Ideas about electrical current commonly held by children.
- Importance of children understanding the scientific conception of electrical current.
- Exploration of scientific conceptions as a context for evaluating the worth of ideas.

Generative Learning Model:

The electrical circuit activity is framed in terms of Osborne and Wittrock's constructivist *Generative Learning Model* (GLM). There are four phases–preliminary, focus, challenge, and application.

Children's Alternative Conceptions About Electrical Current:

The underlying idea children have and may retain is that there is a source such as a battery and a consumer such as a bulb. Electricity stored in the source flows to the bulb where it is 'used up'.

In explaining how electricity is used up by a bulb (or bulbs) children will conceptualize a variety of models. Five of the most common are the one pole no return model, the two-way colliding currents model, the one-way using up model, the sharing model, and the scientific one-way 'not using-up' model.

- One pole, no return model: Electricity flows out of one end of the battery to the bulb.
- Two-way colliding currents model: Electricity flows out of each end of the battery and meets at the bulb.
- One-way using up model: Electricity flows out of one end of the battery, the bulb uses up some of the electricity, and the remaining (less) electricity returns to the other end of the battery. If there are two bulbs, one bulb will be dimmer than the other.
- Sharing model (more than one bulb): Electricity flows out of one end of the battery, the two bulbs share and use up equal amounts of electricity, and the remaining (less) electricity returns to the other end of the battery.
- Scientific one-way: Electricity flows out of one end of the battery (negative end) through the circuit and the same amount of electricity returns to the other end of the battery (positive end).

Preliminary Phase: Finding out Children's Ideas

This phase uses an interview-about-instances survey to find out students' views about electrical current in a simple circuit. The survey is in a multiple-choice format and can be accompanied by diagrams. Each of the seven survey items asks students to choose from four possible responses, three of which are common alternative conceptions and one of which is the scientific conception. A copy of the survey is reproduced at the end of the activity.

The survey addresses three key ideas about electricity:

1. What conditions are required in order for a flow of electricity to occur?

2. How does electricity flow in a directional sense? Does it flow from both ends of the battery or from one end back to the other end?

3. How does electricity flow in a "quantitative" sense? Is there the same amount of current in all parts of the circuit or does a bulb use up some electricity?

Focus Phase: Teacher Guided Activities

This lesson phase provides experiences for students involving simple electrical circuits. Students work in small groups and are given batteries, bulbs, wire, and switches. As the students work, the teacher tries to focus their attention on the three issues of configuration, direction, and quantity. Students:

- Try to make bulbs glow using a battery, bulbs, and insulated wire in various configurations. Bulb and battery holders are useful aids. Students should also integrate switches into their circuits.
- Draw circuits using their own made-up symbols. Students label which circuits work and which do not and hypothesize explanations.
- Share with other group members what they know or have learned.

Challenge Phase: Clarifying, Sharing, Testing, and Restructuring Ideas

In this whole class session:

- Students discuss and clarify their theories on what happens in a simple circuit. The teacher proposes the scientific model as an alternative if no student does. The teacher keeps track of the proposed models. Students are eventually asked to select one model that they think is best.

- Students share ideas. Pairs of students with different views can present evidence in support of their views. Students can make circuits to try and convince others. Class discussion follows with further idea sharing. The teacher notes that the most popular view is not necessarily correct.

- Students test their chosen models in regard to direction and quantity. The teacher focuses the students on the idea of using empirical tests to decide the relative merits of each model. An ammeter is introduced and demonstrated to show how it detects electrical current. The teacher suggests that to test for direction, students should simplify their circuit by only using a battery, two wires, and the ammeter.

- To test direction, the leads are reversed to show that the current can reverse its direction (e.g., needle on analog meter reverses direction, readout on digital meter changes sign from or to -). Findings suggest that the current does travel from one end of the battery through the circuit to the other end. (Another way to test direction is to use four compasses set up on a cardboard platform around a vertical wire (See Firgure B2). When the wires attached to the positive and negative ends of the battery are reversed, all the compass needles change orientation.) A piece of evidence contradicting the one pole, no return model is that one wire attached to the bulb from one end of the battery will not light the bulb.

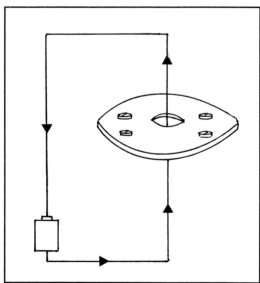

Figure B2

- To test quantity, the teacher and students discuss how two ammeters can be used, one on each side of the battery and bulb (See Figure B3). Students make diagrams of how they could set up a fair test. One ammeter is wired into the circuit and students are asked to predict how the second ammeter will read if

their theory is correct. Only the scientific model survives the quantity test.

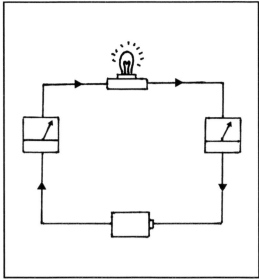

Figure B3

- Students are aided in reconstructing their ideas. Only the scientific model survives the empirical test but it is the least 'believable' by students. Students need help reconstructing their ideas with the help of analogies, similes, metaphors, and models. One way is to represent the flow of electrical current is as a continuous line of train cars on a circular track, with the front of the train is attached to the back. To illustrate the idea that the quantity of electricity in the circuit remains the same in all parts, ask students which cars of the train will slow down when the brake is put on in one car (e.g., all cars).

Application of New Learning:

Students are given new problems to solve using the scientific ideas they have learned. This helps the new ideas gain plausibility. Students work in small groups or pairs. The teacher helps clarify questions, suggests possible avenues of solution, and provides explanations.

- **Configuration.** If one bulb in a group of bulbs connected in series (one continuous path for electricity) is removed no other bulbs will glow. Students are asked to make a series circuit. They are asked to find other ways (parallel circuit with multiple paths) to arrange the bulbs so if one fails the others still glow.

- **Direction:** Students experiment with trying to reverse the direction of rotation of an electric motor.

- **Quantity:** Students test to see if the electric motor 'uses up' electricity.

Survey Questions About Electrical Current

1. A flashlight battery is fully charged but has not yet been placed in the flashlight. It is sitting on a table and is not connected to anything. Is there an electrical current in the battery?

2. An ordinary electric light is fixed to the ceiling. The light bulb has been taken out but the wall switch is on. Is there an electrical current in the bare prongs of the light socket?
    (a) No, because there can't be a current flowing.
    (b) Yes, because if you touch the prongs you get a shock.
    (c) Yes, because if you put the bulb in the socket the bulb would glow.
    (d) Yes, because the current would be going out from the prongs.

3. Two metal rods are connected to the terminals on a battery by two wires. The rods are immersed in a liquid but not touching each other. There IS an electrical current along the wire from the battery to the metal rod. Is there an electrical current in the liquid?
    (a) It depends on what the liquid is.
    (b) There must be a current in the liquid.
    (c) There is no current in the liquid.

4. A flashlight has three batteries in it. The flashlight is switched on and the bulb is glowing. Which of the following ideas best describes the electrical current through the batteries?
    (a) The battery closest to the bulb will have the most current.
    (b) The middle battery of the three will have the most current.
    (c) The battery furthest from the bulb will have the most current.
    (d) The middle battery of the three will have the least current.
    (e) All three batteries will all have the same current.

5. A battery is connected to a bulb by two wires. The bulb is glowing and there is an electrical current in one of the wires (first wire). Which of the following is the best description of the electrical current in the wire (second wire)?
    (a) There is no electrical current in the second wire.
    (b) There is some electrical current in the second wire but less than in the first wire.
    (c) There is the same electrical current in the second wire as in the first wire.
    (d) There is more electrical current in the second wire than in the first wire.

6. In the same situation (above), the electricity is flowing from the battery to the bulb. Which of the following is the best description of the direction of the electrical current in the second wire?
    (a) The current has no direction as there is no current.
    (b) The current is in the direction from the battery to the bulb.
    (c) The current is in the direction from the bulb to the battery.

7. A battery is connected to a bulb by two wires and the bulb is glowing. Which of the following statements best describes the electrical current in the wires? .
    (a) There will be NO current in the wire attached to the base of the battery.
    (b) The electrical current will be in a direction TOWARD the bulb in both wires.
    (c) The direction of the electrical current will be one-way and the current will be LESS in the return wire.
    (d) The direction of the electrical current will be one-way and the current will be the SAME in both wires.

ANSWERS

1. No. The battery is a store of electrical energy but there is no flow of charge.

2. There is no electrical current because there is no complete circuit. If you touch the prongs you complete the circuit and then there will be a current. That's why you get a shock.

3. If there is a current in the wire then there must be an equal current in all parts of the liquid. The liquid must be a conductor otherwise there would be no current in the wire. In the other wire the direction of the current is from rod to battery.

4. All the batteries will have the same current because they are all connected into the same circuit and the flow is equal throughout the circuit.

5. There is the same electrical current in both wires. The bulb is glowing so there is a flow of electricity and the flow is equal throughout the same circuit.

6. The current is in the direction from the bulb to the battery. The current flows one way completely around the circuit.

7. The answer is D.

References

Osborne, R. & Freyberg, P. (1984). *Learning in Science.* Heinemann: New Zealand.

Osborne, R. & Wittrock, M. (1983). Learning Sicence: a generative process. *Science Education, 67*(4), 489-508

Related Website

http://www.amasci.com/miscon/elect.html
This website presents an interesting discussion concerning erroneous ideas about electricity that may be conveyed by school textbooks.

Activity 9

Like, Real Heavy? – Chemical Reactions

Background Information: Chemical reactions can be studied within the Grade 5 topic *Classroom Chemistry*. A chemical reaction is a transformation in which a substance decomposes, or combines with other substances, or interchanges parts of its structure with other substances to form new substances.

At the molecular level, chemical reactions happen when the particles comprising chemicals collide together and the electromagnetic force (i.e., the attraction and repulsion felt by all objects carrying an electric charge) pushes and pulls their electrons and nuclei into new arrangements.

When we combine vinegar (which is 10% acetic acid) and baking soda (which is sodium bicarbonate, a base), they react chemically to create three new products: carbon dioxide gas, sodium carbonate, and water. The reaction takes place in two steps. In the first step, the products are sodium acetate and carbonic acid:

$$HC_2H_3O_2 + NaHCO_3 = NaC_2H_3O_2 + H_2CO_3$$

The carbonic acid then decomposes into carbon dioxide and water:

$$H_2CO_3 = CO_2 + H_2O$$

The carbon dioxide gas is invisible but it can form bubbles and extinguish a flame. Carbon dioxide is also denser than air as evidenced by the fact that it can be poured (downward) onto the candle. In fact, the density of carbon dioxide is 1.56 g/ml while the density of air is only 1.0 g/ml.

Like, Real Heavy!

Materials:

Matches, candle, 2 drinking glasses, vinegar, baking soda, 600 ml beaker, and a spoon.

Procedure:

1. Light the candle and set it in the glass.

2. Pick up the "empty" beaker–which is actually filled with air–and make a pouring motion over the glass containing the candle, as if pouring the air into the glass.

3. Observe the candle.

4. Scoop two tablespoons of baking soda into the beaker.

5. Pour three tablespoons of vinegar into the second (empty) glass.

   (Read the rest of the instructions before proceeding.)

6. Pour the vinegar all at once into the beaker containing the baking soda.

7. Observe what happens to the mixture.

8. After two or three seconds tilt the beaker over the glass containing the candle (like you did with the "empty" beaker) as if pouring into the glass but DO NOT pour any of the liquid mixture into the glass containing the candle.

9. Observe the candle.

Questions:

- What happened to the candle when you poured air onto it? Why?

- What did you observe happening as you added vinegar to baking soda?

- What might explain what you observed happening (above)?

- What happened to the candle when you poured onto it from the beaker after adding the vinegar to the baking soda? Why?

- What do you infer are three properties of what you poured onto the candle? Evidence?

- What do you think is the chemical name of what was poured onto the candle? Why?

Reflection:

What do you think you would need to know about science, teaching, and learning in order to use this activity effectively with children?

Activity 10

Where Are You?

Background Information: Animal camouflage and natural selection can be studied during three topics in the *Alberta Elementary Science Program* (1996) – *Needs of Plants and Animals* (Grade 1), *Small Crawling and Flying Animals* (Grade 2), and *Animal Life Cycles* (Grade 3).

Where Are You?

Materials:

Colored toothpicks (same number of each color).

Procedure:

Record the number of toothpicks of each color. Scatter all the toothpicks in an area, for example, in a grassy field, which has a color similar to one of the toothpick colors. Have the students see how many of the toothpicks they can collect in a designated time. Have them record how many they found of each color.

Observations:

How many of each colored toothpick were found? Make a chart to record your results.

Relationships:

- What color of toothpick was found the most?

- What color of toothpick was found the least?

Generalization:

In general, when you are searching for different colored toothpicks on the ground or on the floor or on any colored surface, which color of toothpick will be the hardest to find?

Explanation:

Why are some colors of toothpicks harder to find than other colors?

Science in Context: Camouflage and Natural Selection

- If you were an animal that ate 'toothpick food', which color of toothpick would survive the longest?

- Which color of toothpick would reproduce more of its own kind and become more numerous?

Activity 11

Explaining the Seasons

Background Information: The four seasons are caused by a combination of the 23.5 degree tilt from the vertical of the Earth's axis and the Earth's orbital motion around the sun. These factors, in turn, determine which of the north or south hemispheres of the Earth receive the sun's energy most directly.

Near June 21 (the summer solstice), the Earth's tilt results in the sun being positioned directly over the Tropic of Cancer at 23.5 degrees north latitude. This places the northern hemisphere more directly in the path of the sun's energy. Alberta is in the northern hemisphere so on June 21 it is warmer and summer officially begins.

Six months later, the Earth has orbited halfway around the sun and the situation is reversed. Near December 21 (the winter solstice), the sun is positioned directly over the Tropic of Capricorn at 23.5 degrees south latitude. Due to the Earth's tilt (which remains the same at a 23.5 degree tilt from the vertical), it is now the southern hemisphere that is more directly in the path of the sun's energy. So Alberta is colder and winter officially begins.

Near March 21 and September 21, the sun is directly over the equator and so its energy is in balance between the northern and southern hemispheres. Alberta then has spring and fall, respectively.

Explaining the Seasons

Alternative Conceptions:

Many students believe that the explanation for the seasons is the distance of the Earth from the sun. They think that the Earth is closer to the sun in summer and further in the winter. Students may also think that the Earth's 24-hour rotation around its axis, which causes day and night, has something to do with the seasons.

One Useful Model:

One way to explain why we have seasons is to use a light bulb and a globe. Set the light bulb on a table and move the globe around it. Be sure to hold the globe at a consistent angle showing the tilt of the Earth. Stop at four points around the table to show the four seasons in Alberta (See Figure B4).

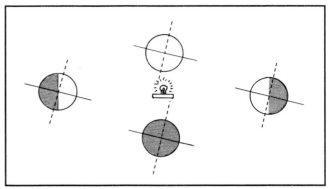

Figure B4

Note that in Figure B4, the left hand globe shows summer in the northern hemisphere and the right hand globe shows winter in the northern hemisphere.

Another Useful Model:

Here is another way to explain the four seasons. Set up an overhead projector so its light shines on a globe. Ensure the projector light and the globe are on the same level. Obtain a piece of masonite with a symmetrical pattern of rows and columns of holes in it as would be the case if it was used to hang hooks on. Place the masonite on the projector so the image of the holes is projected onto the globe (See Figure B5).

Figure B5

Students should be able to see that when the globe is oriented so that Alberta is tilted away from the sun, the circles of light created by the projector appear on Alberta as elongated and dimmed. This represents winter because the less direct sunlight provides less heat to the area. Students also should be able to see that when Alberta is tilted toward the sun, the circles of light created by the projector appear on Alberta as circular and brighter. This represents summer because the more direct sunlight provides more heat to the area.

Reflections:

- How well does each of the two models explain why the sun appears low on the southern horizon in winter and high on the horizon in summer?

- Which of the two models do you think would be more effective in explaining the seasons? Why?

- If you were teaching about the seasons using one (or both) of the models, how would you take into account that most students think that the seasons are caused by the distance of the Earth from the sun?

- What would you need to know about science, teaching, and learning to improve children's understanding about the seasons?

Activity 12

Buoyancy

Background Information: Buoyancy is an important idea related to the *Alberta Elementary Science Program* (1996) topics of *Exploring Liquids* (Grade 2) and *Buoyancy and Boats* (Grade 2). It is also less directly related to *Wetland Ecosystems* (Grade 5). The buoyancy activity goes much more deeply into an understanding of buoyancy than would be expected of elementary school children. However, an important purpose is to provoke thinking about the question of what levels of knowledge are appropriate for the teacher and for students, respectively, when trying to teach science.

Why Objects Float

Essentially, an object floats because it occupies sufficient volume to displace a volume of the fluid (e.g., water) it is floating in that has a weight equal to its own weight. For a ten kilogram object to float, it must occupy sufficient volume (be 'large enough') such that when it is placed in the water it displaces a weight of water equal to ten kilograms. For a 10,000 ton ship to float in the ocean it must be large enough in volume to displace 10,000 tons of water.

When an object is submerged, the water exerts an upward force called the buoyant force that is opposite in direction to the downward force of gravity. That is why it is easier to lift something that is in the water. The origin of the buoyant force is the water itself, which exerts pressure on the object from all directions. The forces are greater at greater depth (we feel these forces when we swim under the water at different depths and scuba divers must wear weighted belts or vests to help counteract the increased buoyant force) so the forces

acting on the bottom of the object are greater than those acting on the top. This creates a net upward force.

When an object is placed in water (or another fluid) it displaces or pushes away some of the water to another location to make room for itself. When the object is completely submerged the volume of the displaced water will equal the volume of the object. When the object is only partially submerged the volume of displaced water will be less than the volume of the object.

The Greek philosopher Archimedes is said to have discovered the principle named in his honor when he got into the bath. The principle is "An immersed object is buoyed up by a force equal to the weight of the water it displaces." Immersed means either completely submerged or partially submerged.

Small (in volume) objects displace small amounts of water and large objects displace large amounts of water. Larger buoyant forces then, act on larger objects. The volume of the object and not its weight determines the buoyant force. And whether an object sinks or floats has to do with how great the buoyant force is compared to the object's weight. When the buoyant force is greater than the weight of the object, then the object floats. When the buoyant force is less than the weight the object, then the object sinks.

The density relationship compares the volume of an object to its weight so it is a shortcut for determining whether an object will sink or float. The density is calculated by dividing the weight (mass) of the object by its volume (M/V). The density must be compared with the density of the fluid. Water's density is 1.0, so an object with a density less than 1.0 will float in water. Other liquids (e.g., salt water, alcohol) have lesser or greater densities than water. An object that does float in a liquid (e.g., water) may float in a denser liquid (e.g., salt water).

How Can Something This Big Float?

Materials:

250 ml graduated cylinder, 25 ml graduated cylinder, square of dark paper, 300 ml beaker full of water, 140 ml beaker, 30 ml plastic vial (fits inside graduated cylinder), vial cap with pull thread attached, eye dropper, small marbles, small steel ball, electronic balance, and centimetre cubes.

Important Information About Water:

1 millilitre (ml) of water = 1 cubic centimeter (cc) of water = 1 gram of water (weight).

Preparation:

- Fill a 250 ml graduated cylinder with water exactly to the 210 ml mark. Use the medicine dropper to be precise. Read the graduated cylinder at eye level at the bottom of the meniscus. A square of dark paper placed behind the graduated cylinder may help.

- Weigh the capped empty vial and enter the weight in Column 1, Row 2 (see the Data Chart at the end of this activity).

Measuring the Volume of the Capped Vial:

- Measure the volume of the capped vial, i.e., the volume of space that it occupies.

- What generalization can you make about measuring the volume of an object using displacement? Test your generalization using centimetre cubes. Revise your generalization if necessary.

- Enter the volume for the capped vial in all columns across Row 1.

Investigating Displacement:

- Read the Data Chart at the end of this activity and gather and record the required data by first preparing

the vial as indicated at the top of each column. After preparing the vial (capped!), weigh it and record the new weight.

- Lower the prepared vial into the 250 ml graduated cylinder until it stabilizes in the water (floats or sinks) with no outside support. Record the volume of water displaced by the vial (in mls) by reading the graduated cylinder again and recording whether the vial sinks or floats. Calculate the density of the vial by dividing the weight (mass) by the volume and record the density. (e.g., weight of empty vial and lid = 4.6gm, volume of vial and lid = 25.4 cc, density of empty vial and lid = 4.6/24.5 = 0.181gm/cm^3).

- Remove the vial and repeat the above procedure for the first six columns until all required data are entered. Do not do Column 7–you will be asked to predict what your findings will be (see below).

Finding Patterns in the Volume/Weight/Displacement Data:

- What patterns do you see in the data that might help you explain why an object floats?

Predicting:

- Based on the patterns you have discerned, make predictions for Column 7 (full of water). Predict the weight, the displacement, and whether the vial will sink or float. Then test your predictions by collecting the required data.

DATA CHART

	Empty Vial	1 Marble in vial	2 Marbles	3 Marbles	4 Marbles	Steel Ball	Full of Water
Volume Vial & lid (cc)							
Weight (Mass) of vial & lid (gm)							
Displace-ment (ml) volume							
Float or Sink?							
Density M/V							

• Compare your results for Column 7 with your predictions. How do you explain the similarities/differences?

Explaining:

• At what point do the volume of the vial and the amount of water displaced become equal? Why do you think that is?

• How do you explain why an object floats?

• What evidence do you have from your tests to support your claim?

• How could you test your explanation?

Activity 13

Felt Pen Secrets

Background Information: Chromatography, invented in 1903, means "colour writing". It is a technique used to identify chemicals through colour separation. Applications of chromatography include testing liquid mixtures (e.g., drugs and dyes), testing the purity of foods and water, and investigating crime scenes (e.g., *Evidence and Investigations* – Grade 6).

Chromatography is a practical application of concepts related to solubility and capillary action. With respect to solubility, and the felt pens used in the following activity:

• The black pigment of the marker will dissolve in certain solvents.

• Non-permanent markers are soluble in water.

• Permanent markers are insoluble in water but soluble in Isopropyl alcohol (Isopropanol), commonly known as rubbing alcohol [$(CH_3)_2CHOH$].

• If the black pigment of the marker is soluble, the solvent will carry along the molecules of pigment as it moves up the filter paper.

Other ideas about capillary action will come into play during the felt pens activity:

• The solvent and the dissolved pigment molecules move up the paper through capillary action, which operates against the force of gravity.

• Capillary action is the tendency for a liquid to be drawn up the inside of a thin tube.

• Capillary action occurs when the adhesive forces (molecules of liquid sticking to a surface) exceed the cohesive forces (molecules of liquid sticking to each other).

• In our activity, the solvent molecules move up because they are attracted to the particles in the filter paper.

• The narrower the tube, the higher the liquid will climb because a narrow column weighs less than a thick one.

• A plant makes use of capillary action to draw liquid water into its system.

During the felt pen activity, colour separation can be achieved because of the following related ideas.

• The black pigment may be made up of a mixture of different colored pigments.

• The upward movement of the solvent/ink mixture separates out the hidden pigments of the black ink.

• The pigments can be separated because they are in a mixture, not chemically combined.

• As the pigment chemicals travel up the paper by capillary action, some move faster than others.

• Different colored pigments get carried along at different rates and for different distances because the molecules of some pigments are bigger and heavier than the molecules of others.

• Heavier pigments separate out first, lighter ones separate out further up the piece of paper.

• The separation of the pigments creates the distinct colored bands on the filter paper.

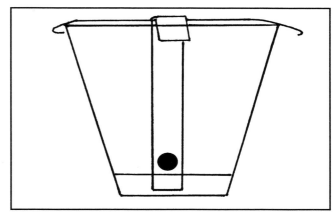

Figure B6

Felt Pen Secrets

Materials:

Four black felt tip pens: Crayola™, Mr.Sketch™, Sanford Sharpie™, Sanford King Size™, 2 circles of filter paper (or coffee filters), 8 clear plastic cups (210 ml capacity), 8 paper clips, 2 pairs of scissors, 2 rulers, 2 pencils, masking tape, glue stick, 4 Petri dishes or lids, 2 magnifiers, water, Isopropyl alcohol (rubbing alcohol).

Warning:

Isopropyl alcohol requires safe handling procedures.

Procedure:

1. You will need two setups for **each** felt pen, one using water as a solvent and the other using Isopropyl alcohol as a solvent.

2. Be sure to label each of your setups so that you can identify the pen and the solvent.

3. Fold a filter circle lightly in half, then unfold. Use the fold line as a guide to help you draw 4 strips 1 cm by 9 cm. Make a pencil line across all four strips 1 cm from the bottom and another pencil line 1 cm from the top. Cut out the 4 strips. Make 4 more strips from the other filter circle.

4. You will use each of the four pens to make a dot on two different strips. In other words, you will dot two strips with Crayola, two strips with Mr. Sketch, etc. Make each dot a heavy .5 cm (5 mm) diameter dot about .5 cm above (that is, toward the middle of the strip) one pencil line. Fold the strip along the other pencil line to create a "hook".

Recording Felt Pen Data

Felt Pen Identification	Observations During Chromatography
Crayola™	Water
	Alcohol
Mr. Sketch™	Water
	Alcohol

Sharpie™	Water	
	Alcohol	
King Size™	Water	
	Alcohol	

5. Straighten out each paper clip and lay one across the top of each glass. Using the folded paper "hook", hang a filter paper strip from each wire, in the centre of each glass. The black dot will be at the bottom end of each strip.

6. Carefully add water to 4 glasses, each with a different pen dot. Add just enough solvent to reach the bottom pencil line, ensuring that the solvent level does not quite reach the black dot. Do not get water on the rest of the strip (See Figure B6).

7. Carefully add alcohol to the other 4 glasses to the bottom pencil line, ensuring that the solvent level does not quite reach the black dot. Do not get alcohol on the rest of the strip. Cover each alcohol glass with a Petri dish or dish lid (to control evaporation).

8. Let all 8 setups stand for the next 15 minutes and observe.

Explanations:

- Why do some ink dots change and others do not?
- Why does the water/ink climb the paper strip?
- Why do some strips show colors and others do not?

Activity 14

Paper Towels – Thinking About Performance Assessment

Background: This open-ended activity is an opportunity to design a performance assessment for students. The activity fits well with the *Alberta Elementary Science Program* (1996) topics *Exploring Liquids* (Grade 2) and *Testing Materials and Design* (Grade 3).

Paper Towels – Thinking About Performance Assessment

Materials:

3 kinds of paper towel with different designs and different absorbencies, watch with second hand, eye droppers, beakers or measuring cups of various sizes, scissors, magnifying glass, 3 plastic cups (7 oz/210 ml), ruler, tweezers, 3 Petri dishes, 3 foil trays, and 2 funnels.

Task:

You will find out which of three different kinds of paper towels is the most absorbent and which is the least absorbent. You will design and carry out your inquiry using some or all of the materials listed above.

Response Format:

- What steps did you follow in your procedure? List them.
- Which of the following did you do during your investigation?

___ Make all the paper towels the same size.

___ Make all the paper towels completely wet.

___ Use the same amount of water to get each towel wet

___ Let each towel soak in the water for the same length of time.

- What evidence from your investigation led you to conclude which towel absorbs the most water and how did you know which towel absorbs the least water?
- Do all the towels have to be completely wet to get an accurate result? Why?

Scoring System:

Design your own scoring rubric that takes into account both the process and product of the investigation.

Reference

Brown, J., & Shavelson, R. (1996). *Assessing Hands-On Science.* Thousand Oaks CA: Corwin Press (Sage).

Activity 15

Floating and Sinking – Prediction, Observation, and Explanation

Background Information: The purpose of this activity is to provide you with an opportunity to apply your knowledge of buoyancy in order to explain an event. An additional purpose is to provide you with an example of how a Prediction-Observation-Explanation (POE) framework can be used for teaching, learning, and assessing understanding. Children can explore ideas about floating and sinking in the Grade 2 topic *Buoyancy and Boats.*

Floating and Sinking: POE

Materials:

Two beakers or large glasses, water, clear pop such as ginger ale (unopened), and some dry raisins.

Predict:

- How will raisin behave when placed in water/
- How will a raisin behave when place in ginger ale?
- Will there be a difference in how a raisin behaves in pop and in water?
- Why do you think so?

Procedure:

Fill one container full with water and fill the other container with the pop. Place 5-7 raisins in each container.

Observations:

- How did the raisins behave when placed in water?
- How did the raisins behave when placed in pop?
- If there was a difference between how the raisins behaved in water versus the pop, what was this difference?
- Draw how the raisins behaved in water.
- Draw how the raisins behaved in pop.

Explanation:

- Why do you think the raisins behaved as they did in water?
- Why do you think the raisins behaved as they did in the pop?
- Explain why the raisins in the water behaved differently from those in the pop.
- What did you observe to make you think your explanation is accurate?
- How would you test your explanation to try to verify it?

Technological Problem Solving Activities

Technological
Problem
Solving
Activities

Activity 16

Building Art Straw Towers and Bridges

Background Information: Tower and bridge building activities can be found in the *Alberta Elementary Science Program* (1996) in the Grade 3 topics *Building With a Variety of Materials* and *Testing Materials and Designs*. These activities allow children a context in which to develop a conceptual understanding of structural strength and stability.

Art Straw Towers and Bridges Activity

Tower Building:

Build a tower out of the least number of art straws possible. Your tower should be at least 2 m tall, should not tip over and should support a film canister of sand. After you have completed your tower, answer the following questions:

- What do you notice about the general shape of your tower?
- What do you notice about the base of your tower?
- What did you do in order to make your tower strong? Stable?
- How many paper straws did you use?

Bridge Building:

Build a bridge out of the fewest number of art straws possible that will span a gap of 50 cm and support at least ten washers. After you have completed your bridge, answer the following questions:

- What did you do in order to make your bridge strong?
- What is the general pattern of your bridge?
- How may paper straws did you use?

Summary Discussion:

- What needs are met by towers and bridges you see in everyday life?
- What cultural and social priorities and values are reflected in our need for towers and bridges?
- How were your thinking, talking, and designing influenced by the way these building tasks were set?
- How would you describe the planning and designing that occurred as you carried out these tasks?
- How did you evaluate your designs as you went along?
- How would you assess children who completed these same activities in your classroom?

When working with adults in post-secondary courses, instructors present activities that have been modified for preservice teachers. The following sample lesson sequence is intended to provide you with insight into how building art straw towers might be taught to children in school classrooms. Note the increased structure and time that is needed in order to work children through technological problem-solving activities.

Children Building Art Straw Towers – A Sample Lesson Sequence

Initial Lessons:

- Engage the children in thinking about towers. Help them connect towers with ideas from previous lessons.
- Explore the children's existing ideas about towers. Where have they seen towers? What kinds of towers have they seen? Have they ever built towers using play materials?
- Have the children locate library books about towers. Have the children do Internet searches.
- Explore some tower vocabulary: base, load, strength, stability
- Have children identify the needs that are being met by towers. How are towers used in our culture?

Introducing the Problem and Naming the Task:

- How can they make a tower out of the least number of straws possible? (If you wish, set some additional criteria such as the finished height and the ability to support some load.) Remember that your task setting will affect the children's talking, thinking, and eventual performance.
- Use a teacher-guided conversation to explore why it is important to be economical with materials. Relate this discussion to the notion of how engineers strive to propose elegant solutions to problems. An elegant solution is one in which you are able to solve the problem and produce a reliable, durable product that costs the least amount of money. Talk about the economics behind marketing a product.
- What existing ideas do the children already have about how to build their towers?
- Invite the children to explore the art straws and share ideas about how to join them together.

- Record the children's suggestions on a chart for future reference.

- Have a teacher-guided conversation about potential challenges: How will they keep their tower from tipping over? How will they add strength to their tower without using a lot of materials? How will they keep track of the amount of art straws they use? How can they do ongoing tests of their design? What kinds of problems do they anticipate? What is troubleshooting?

Anticipatory Planning: Using Drawings to Visualize the Tower and Generate Ideas

- Have children draw and label an initial sketch of their towers. (Children can include measurements and details such as how they are joining straws together.)

- Have teacher-guided conversations in which the children share their plans and the reasons for the choices they made. Why did they choose certain methods of joining? Why did they choose a certain overall design?

Making and Testing the Tower:

- Have the children make and test the towers that appear in their sketched plans.

- Have teacher-guided conversations about the challenges they encountered. Have each child talk about and show their design problems. Introduce the term "troubleshooting". Encourage children to offer solutions to other children's design problems.

- Develop a sense of camaraderie: All designers run into challenges and have to solve ongoing problems.

- Help the children understand why some towers (or all!) were strong and stable: Review ideas such as: center of gravity, symmetry, keeping the weight over the base, have a wider base than top, sinking the legs into the ground, adding feet, splaying the supports, cross bracing, square bracing, bundling, guy lines, and joint reinforcement. Have the children use the towers to point out each of these ideas and encourage them to think about why these were useful design ideas.

- Have the children re-design and re-test their towers to make them better.

- Encourage the children to keep a record of their alternative designs.

Final Lessons:

- Have children talk about any new towers they have made. Have them identify improvements made and why these were good ideas.

- Have the children talk about how they overcame design obstacles. Revisit the ideas of troubleshooting.

- Have them summarize what makes a good tower. Have them identify these same attributes in towers that are part of their everyday lives.

- Have the children talk about what further design changes they would make to improve their towers even more.

- Have the children talk about what other activities they would like to do with towers.

Activity 17
Building Parachutes

Background Information: Parachute building is a common activity with children that fits with the *Alberta Elementary Science Program* (1996) Grade 6 topic of *Flight*. Through building parachutes, children can learn about the following ideas:

- The shape of an object moving through air influences the strength of different forces that act upon it.

- Control of the parachute can be achieved by controlling the airflow around it.

- Air that gets trapped in the parachute canopy gets compressed and exerts more pressure than the rest of the air around it. This pressure pushes up and helps counteract the pull of gravity.

- Many factors can influence the parachute: the shape of the canopy, the material of the canopy, the length of the shroud lines, the type of shroud line, the kind of weight attached to the shroud lines, the weight of the canopy, and the height from which the parachute is dropped. All of these factors can form the focus of future investigations with children.

Parachute Building Activity

Design and make a parachute that will support a washer and fall as slowly as possible. Test the parachute.

Materials:

fabric scraps	string
clay	pieces of plastic
tissue	paper
washers	thread
cardboard	aluminum foil
paper clips	balloons

Tools:

scissors
glue gun & white glue
rulers
hole punch
tape: scotch and masking
pencils
sewing needle

Activity Questions:

1. What happened when you tested your parachute?

2. What challenges did you encounter when making and testing your parachute?

3. What would you now do to improve your parachute?

Assessment Questions to Think About:

- If you had your students complete this parachute activity, how would you assess:
- Conceptual Understanding?
- The Thinking in Action (Skills)?
- Children's Attitude Development?
- The Parachute?

When working with adults in post-secondary courses, instructors present activities that have been modified for preservice teachers. The following sample lesson sequence is intended to provide you with insight into how parachute building might be taught to children in school classrooms. Note the increased structure and time that is needed in order to work children through technological problem-solving activities.

Parachute Building With Children

Initial Lessons:

- Engage the children in thinking about parachutes and help them develop a sense of ownership for parachutes. Help them connect parachutes with ideas from previous lessons.

- Have teacher-guided conversations with the children about parachutes.

- Have the children locate library books about parachutes. Have the children do Internet searches.

- Explore some parachute vocabulary: canopy, shroud lines, load

- Have the children identify the needs that are being met by parachutes. How are parachutes used in our culture?

Introducing the Problem and Naming the Task:

- How can you make a model parachute that will support a washer and fall as slowly as possible?

- What existing ideas do the children already have about how to solve this problem?

- Invite the children to explore the materials and make predictions about their future use.

- Have teacher-guided conversations about potential challenges: How do they think they might join materials together? How will they decide upon the length of the shroud lines? What materials will they use? How will they test their designs? How will they make a parachute that drops in a controlled fashion?

Anticipatory Planning: Using Drawings to Visualize the Parachute and Generate Ideas

- Have children draw and label an initial sketch of their parachutes. (Children can include measurements and details such as how they are attaching the shroud lines to the canopy.)

- Have teacher-guided conversations in which the children share their plans and the reasons for the choices they made. Why did they choose certain materials? Why did they choose certain canopy designs? Why did they choose to join shroud lines to the canopy in the way that they did?

• Understand that your task setting will affect the children's talking, thinking, and eventual performance. Remember that children need to practice different kinds of tasks (very open tasks, tasks with some constraints, and tightly defined tasks) during the course of the entire *Flight* unit.

My Sketched Plan:

Making and Testing the Parachute:

• Have the children make and test the parachute that appears in their sketched plans.

• Have teacher-guided conversations about the challenges they encountered. Have children talk about and show their design problems. Introduce the term "troubleshooting". Encourage children to offer solutions to other children's design problems.

• Develop a sense of camaraderie: All designers run into challenges and have to solve ongoing problems.

• Help children understand the science behind the technology.

• Have the children re-design and re-test their parachutes to make them better.

• Encourage the children to keep a record of their alternative designs.

Changes to My Initial Design (Opportunistic Planning):

Final Lessons:

• Have the children talk about how they overcame design obstacles. Revisit the idea of troubleshooting.

• Have them consider what makes a good parachute.

• Have the children think about what further design changes they would make to improve their parachutes.

• Have the children talk about what other activities they would like to do with parachutes.

Activity 18
Building Powered Vehicles

Background Information: These activities involving building model vehicles are related to two topics in the *Alberta Elementary Science Program* (1996): *Building Devices and Vehicles That Move* (Grade 4) and *Mechanisms That Use Electricity* (Grade 5). The intent of this series of activities is to help you:

• Gain familiarity with tools and materials used in design technology activities.

• Experience some of the skills involved in doing design technology (e.g., designing and re-designing, building models, evaluating designs, etc.).

• Re-visit ideas related to fair tests.

• In the future, help you compare doing design technology activities with 'found' materials versus using kit materials such as LEGO.

Building Powered Vehicles: Gravity, Wind, and Electricity
Part A: Building Gravity, Wind, and Electricity Vehicles

1. Construct a wood chassis (frame) with mitered corners that can be used as the basis for a gravity powered, wind powered, and electricity powered vehicle. Use a 3 1/2 inch by 5 inch index card as a guide for the size of your wood chassis.

2. Add axles and wheels to your chassis. Think carefully about how to attach these components to the chassis and whether you want the axles or the wheels (or both) to rotate.

3. Test your gravity-powered vehicle and evaluate the design.

4. Now, modify the vehicle so that it becomes a wind-powered vehicle.

5. Test your wind-powered vehicle and evaluate the design.

6. Modify your wind-powered vehicle so that it now becomes a electricity-powered vehicle.

7. Test your electricity-powered vehicle and evaluate the design.

Part B: Optional Activity

8. Should time allow, modify your vehicle and show motion through rubber bands.

When working with adults in post-secondary courses, instructors present activities that have been modified for preservice teachers. The following sample lesson sequence is intended to provide you with insight into how building a gravity-powered vehicle might be taught to children in school classrooms. Note the increased structure and time that is needed in order to work children through technological problem-solving activities.

Children Building Gravity Powered Vehicles – A Sample Lesson Sequence

Lesson #1: Naming the Task / Defining the Global Picture of the Problem /

Drawing and Making the Frame (60 minutes)

- Give children four pieces of pre-cut wood (straight cut) sealed in a plastic bag.
- Provide children with the time to draw and label a chassis design.
- Teacher-guided discussion: What need is met by vehicles? Why do we value vehicles in our society?
- State the problem: How will we join wheels and axles to the chassis? Encourage children to make suggestions (e.g., drilling holes in the frame, using pipe cleaners, straws, clothespins, paper triangles, tape, glue)
- Have the children model their suggestions using manipulatives. Ask other children what they think of the suggestions.
- Record the children's suggestions on a chart for future reference.

Lesson #2: Visualizing the Path Ahead (120 minutes)

- Review suggestions from the chart prepared in the previous lesson. Ask children what they plan to do.

- Have a teacher-guided discussion about the task ahead: Have questions prepared so that you can ask the children about the procedural knowledge (What will you do … How will you …), and strategic knowledge (sequencing of sub-tasks; consequences of decision making such as gluing wheels or gluing axles). Have the children model their suggestions using manipulatives.
- Encourage the children to think about the nature of design practice, the inevitability of design challenges (What kind of problems can you see?; How can a plan help?; How can we overcome problems? What is troubleshooting?).
- Have the children collect their chosen materials, draw a plan, and commence construction.

Lesson #3: Reflecting on Vehicle Construction (90 minutes)

- Have the children use manipulatives to model their ongoing design challenges to the group.
- Ask children to provide advice about how to solve design difficulties. Remind them of the term "troubleshooting."
- Have children share ideas about successful building strategies and design options.
- Have children talk about why they made the decisions they did.
- Help children begin to develop an eye for detail (Let's look again at …).
- Revisit the need for patience, and how frustration and struggle is commonplace in design practice.
- Have the children continue vehicle construction.

Lesson #4: Reflecting on Paths Taken (40 minutes)

- Have a teacher-guided discussion in which the children recall problems encountered and the solutions to those problems.
- Have the children share ideas about any ongoing or remaining difficulties.
- Revisit the importance of troubleshooting.
- Ask, "If you were now given more time and different materials, how would you add to or change your vehicle?"

Activity 19

Shopping Bag – Design Improvement

Background Information: During technological problem-solving lessons, children can also be asked to improve existing technological objects and devices. This activity provides an opportunity to examine a typical paper shopping bag (with handles) and then design an improved shopping bag using any available materials. The activity fits well with *Alberta Elementary Science Program* (1996) topics *Building Things* (Grade 1) and *Testing Materials and Designs* (Grade 3). It also relates to *Trees and Forests* (Grade 6).

Shopping Bag – Design Improvement

Evaluating the Product:

Examine the shopping bag carefully. You may take it apart if you need to.

- What are the purposes of the product?
- How well does the product achieve its purpose?
- What are the product's strengths?
- What are the product's weaknesses?
- How could the product be improved?

Design Drawings:

- Make labeled drawings of your improved design.
- Explain why your design is an improvement over the previous design.

Making a Model:

Gather the required materials and create a model of your improved shopping bag.

Presenting:

Present your improved model to others and explain why your new design is better than the previous design. Be sure to ask for constructive comments from your audience as to the merits and shortcomings of your improved design.

Revising the Design:

Incorporate the useful comments from your peers into a final design and model.

STS Decision-Making Activities

STS Decision-Making Activities

Part B

Activity 20

Environmental Studies Activities for the Schoolyard

Background Information: The schoolyard is an area that should be included in your science program. Through participation in outdoor experiences, children can grow towards understanding concepts and develop appropriate skills and attitudes. Typical content for these outdoor experiences can include studies of plants, animals, snow, soil, and weather.

Elementary children need guidance before beginning schoolyard studies. All schoolyard experiences should be prefaced by pre-activity discussions in which existing ideas are discussed, specific tasks are outlined, time limits are set, behavior and safety rules are reviewed, and methods for recording information are agreed upon. After the schoolyard experience, children should be gathered together to review and share their results and to decide upon future explorations.

The following activities can be linked with the *Alberta Elementary Science Program* (1996) topics: *Seasonal Changes* (Grade 1), *Needs of Plants and Animals* (Grade 1), *Small Crawling and Flying Animals* (Grade 2), *Rocks and Minerals* (Grade 3), *Animal Life Cycles* (Grade 3), *Plant Growth and Changes* (Grade 4), *Waste and Our World* (Grade 4), and *Weather Watch* (Grade 5).

Environmental Studies Activities for the Schoolyard

Part A: Observation Hikes (a typical Division I activity)

1. Touch hike: Look for and touch natural objects to see how they feel. Record and describe these objects.

2. Color hike: Record objects of the following colors: red, blue, green, blue, brown, orange, purple, black, white, tan, yellow, gray.

3. Sound hike: Find a place to sit with your group on the grass. Remain in this location for 5 minutes and listen for all the sounds you can hear. Afterwards, record what you have heard. If you can't identify what made a sound, describe a sound instead.

4. Shape hike: Look for natural shapes (not human built). Find two of each of the following: circle, square, rectangle, triangle, oval, diamond.

Part B: Plot Studies (Division I or II)

- Measure out a 1 m square plot of the school ground. Use your hand lens to assist taking a census of things in the plot (e.g., plant life, invertebrates, signs of animals, rocks, etc.).

- Is there some evidence of human impact on the plot? Describe.

- How could you help children develop an attitude of responsibility toward the environment? What personal actions could they take?

- How could children use their plots year round?

References

Bosak, S.V. (1991). Science is .... (2nd Edition). ON: Scholastic.

Guilbert, S. & Rowell, P. (1996). Plant growth and changes. University of Alberta: Centre for Mathematics, Science and Technology Education.

Hovey, L. & Whitfield, E. (1980). Schoolyard science experiences. Science and Children, 17(7), 44.

Jenness, M. (1987). Schoolyard hikes. Science and Children, 24(6), 23-25.

Van Deman, B.A. (1982). Take a hike! Science and Children, 19(7), 26-27.

Related Website

FEESA, an Environmental Education Society
http://www.info@feesa.ab.ca

Activity 21

Paper Usage

Background Information: This activity requires students to think about how paper is used in the classroom and think about the following concepts:

- Resource supply is finite (e.g., amount of fossil fuels).
- Practicing the 3 Rs (recycle, reuse, and reduce) can help extend finite resources.
- Resources are required to meet the needs and wants of populations.

This activity fits well with the *Alberta Elementary Science Program* (1996) topic *Waste and Our World* (Grade 4).

Paper Usage

Question:

How much paper does the class use in a week, and how is the paper used?

Researching:

- What do you already know about paper use in your class?
- Try to find answers to the following questions: What resources are used to manufacture paper? What other industries are economically dependent on the manufacture of paper? How have people tried to reduce the amount of paper they use? What other ways are available to store and record ideas? What resources are used to manufacture these alternative ways to store and record ideas? What are the drawbacks of using these alternative ways to store and record ideas?

Planning:

- To monitor paper use in your class, you will have to answer the following questions: What are the different kinds of paper used in your class? What are the ways in which each kind of paper is used? How much of each kind of paper is used in each way?

Making Observations and Recording Data:

- What will you observe (i.e., what are the data)?
- Construct a chart to record the data. The chart should allow for different types of paper, different usages for each type, and the daily amount for each usage.
- What kinds of anecdotal records will help to interpret trends in paper use?

Evaluating and Extending the Results:

- How much paper of each type did your class use? What types of usage predominated for each type of paper? What activities resulted in days with high paper use? low paper use?
- Which day of the week featured the highest paper use? the lowest?
- How should paper be used in your classroom? If everyone quit using paper, could you cope? Should you reduce the amount of paper used in your classroom, and how could you do so?
- How much paper do you think is used by your whole school in a week?

Activity 22

Renewable and Nonrenewable Resources

Background Information: This activity requires students to think about the following concepts:

- Resources are required to meet the needs and wants of populations.
- Some resources are derived from earth's resources (e.g., food, fuel, and building materials).
- Environmental changes can occur naturally or be influenced by humans (e.g., through erosion, earthquakes, landslides, overpopulation, pollution, urban growth, and waste disposal).

Students use the context of soil to debate how renewable and nonrenewable resources should be categorized. This activity fits well with the *Alberta Elementary Science Program* (1996) topics *Waste and Our World* (Grade 4) and *Rocks and Minerals* (Grade 3).

Renewable and Nonrenewable Resources

Question:

Is soil a renewable or nonrenewable resource?

Materials:

A variety of soil types (e.g., soils with varying amounts of clay, sand, and silt).

Researching:

- What do you already know about natural resources that can be classified as nonrenewable or renewable? What do you already know about soil?

- Try to find answers to the following questions: What resources are classified as nonrenewable and renewable? How are these classifications made? What are some characteristics of soil? How do the characteristics of soil relate to the difference between renewable and nonrenewable resources? What issues surround renewable and nonrenewable resources? How are resources linked to survival?

Planning:

- To debate with others about whether soil is a renewable or nonrenewable resource, you will need to answer the following questions: What rules will you use for your debate? How will you prepare for the debate? Who will judge the outcome of the debate?

Making Observations and Recording the Data:

- How did the judges decide who won the debate? What records did they need to keep?

Evaluating and Extending the Results:

- What arguments arose during the debate? What issues related to the use of renewable and nonrenewable resources were identified?

- Was soil judged to be renewable or nonrenewable? Was it difficult to make this judgment or was the answer obvious?

- How should we care for soil resources? What could happen if we fail to care for soil resources?

Activity 23

Using Synthetic Chemical Fertilizer Versus Natural Fertilizer to Enhance Plant Growth

Background Information: The following activity requires children to consider the following concepts:

- Some resources are derived from earth's resources (e.g., food, fuel, and building materials).

- Human innovation can have varying benefits and drawbacks (e.g., vaccines, pesticides, and herbicides).

- Science and technology are interdependent and embedded in the societal context (e.g., science influences technology and technology influences science; both science and technology are influenced by social factors and, in turn, influence society).

The activity requires children to conduct a fair test as they work to compare the affect of different fertilizers on plant growth. A simple plant to use in this activity is the Wisconsin Fast Plant (*Brassica rapa*). This plant is a variety of canola bred to go through its life cycle rapidly. It can be grown successfully in ordinary containers in large, sunny, south-facing windows. You can find information on these plants in *Plant Growth and Development* in the *Science and Technology for Children* series.

This activity fits well with the *Alberta Elementary Science Program* (1996) topic *Plant Growth and Changes* (Grade 4).

Using Synthetic Chemical Fertilizer Versus Natural Fertilizer to Enhance Plant Growth

Question:

How do different kinds of fertilizer affect plant growth?

Materials:

Synthetic chemical fertilizer, compost or manure, and two plants of the same kind and of similar size and health (e.g., two bean plants or two Wisconsin Fast Plants [Brassica rapa]).

Safety Note:

Children should wear hand protection when handling fertilizers.

Researching:

- What do you already know about using fertilizers to help plants grow?

- Try to find answers to the following questions: What kinds of synthetic chemical fertilizers are available? How are these fertilizers manufactured? What resources are used in their manufacture? What impact do these fertilizers have on the environment? What kinds of fertilizers are derived from natural plant and animal material? How are these fertilizers prepared for use? What impact do these fertilizers have on the environment?

Planning:

- Apply synthetic chemical fertilizer to one plant and compost or manure to another plant.

- To make this a fair experiment, you will have to answer the following questions: What is the one factor that changes from test to test (i.e., what is the manipulated, or independent, variable)? What will you have to keep the same from test to test (i.e., what are the controlled variables)? What is the outcome that you hope to measure (i.e., what is the responding, or dependent, variable)?

- How will you keep track of plant growth and appearance? How will you avoid damaging the plants with too much fertilizer?

Observing and Recording the Data:

- What will you try to observe (i.e., what are the data)? How frequently will you observe the plants?

- Construct a chart to record the data. The chart should include type of fertilizer, dates when you applied fertilizer, amount of fertilizer applied, size of plants, and appearance of plants. Can you think of any other information that should be included in the chart?

- What kind of anecdotal records and drawings might be useful in analyzing and interpreting the data?

Evaluating and Extending the Results:

- Which plant grew best? What indicated this to you?

- What type of fertilizer should you personally use (e.g., for your house plants or for the plants in your garden)?

- How much would it cost you to use each type of fertilizer?

- What type of fertilizer should be used by farmers who need a lot of fertilizer? Why would you make this recommendation?

- What are the trade-offs between enhancing plant growth and impact on the environment?

Related Website

Science and Technology for Children (STC)
http://www.si.edu.nsrc/pubs/stc/overv.htm

Activity 24

How Computer Games Affect Children – The Responsibility of Scientists and Technologists

Background Information: This activity requires students to consider the following concepts:

- Science and technology are interdependent and embedded in the societal context (e.g., science influences technology and technology influences science; both science and technology are influenced by social factors and, in turn, influence society).

- Technology influences society through its associated products and processes (e.g., vehicles, computers, and clothing).

- Social needs, attitudes, and values influence the direction of technological innovation (e.g., we value fitness, and therefore we have fitness machines).

When using this activity with children, have the children monitor their computer game playing over a month. What are the trade-offs involved in spending various amounts of time playing these games? Challenge the children not to play their games for a month and write down how that affected them (e.g., were they bored? did they find other interesting things to do? will they go back to playing computer games as much as before? etc.).

This activity fits well with the *Alberta Elementary Science Program* (1996) topic *Mechanisms Using Electricity* (Grade 5)and can also be used in conjunction with *Problem Solving Through Technology* units in which you want to emphasize the connection between technology and society.

How Computer Games Affect Children—The Responsibility of Scientists and Technologists

Question:

What responsibility do technologists and scientists have for the ways computer games can affect children?

Materials:

Popular computer game.

Researching:

- What do you already know about the ways in which playing computer games can affect children?

- Try to find answers to the following questions: What computer games are children playing? How much time do children spend playing these games? What health issues might be connected to playing these games? What benefits do children gain through playing these games? How have computer games influenced children in their relationships to other people? What industries are economically dependent on the manufacture and marketing of computer games? What resources are used to manufacture these games? What need is being met by computer games?

Planning:

- To debate with others about whether or not technologists and scientists have a responsibility for the ways computer games can affect children, you will need to answer the following questions: What rules will you use for your debate? How will you prepare for the debate? Who will judge the outcome of the debate?

Making Observations and Recording the Data:

- How did the judges decide who won the debate? What records did they need to keep?

Evaluating and Extending the Results:

- What arguments arose during the debate? What issues related to children's lives were identified?

- Were scientists and technologists judged to have some level of responsibility for the effects of their work? Was it difficult to make this judgment or was the answer obvious? Why?

- Would you buy computer games for your own children? What would influence you in making this decision?

- What suggestions do you have for how computer games should be designed and marketed?

Part C
Overview of Subject Matter Knowledge and Typical Classroom Activities

Note:

This section of the **Companion Manual** is intended to provide an overview of ideas presented in the **Common Framework of Science Learning Outcomes** (1997) a publication that has been used to inform the scope and sequence of provincial elementary school science programs. Ideas are organized under six main concept areas - **Physical Science, Life Science, Earth and Space Science, Technological Structures and Devices, Nature of and Relationship Between Science and Technology,** and **Social and Environmental Contexts of Science and Technology**. In order to help readers revisit and expand their conceptual understanding of subject matter knowledge and understand how these ideas are used with children, the following features have been provided for each of the six main concept areas:

- A brief overview of important organizing ideas that underpin that area.

- A story that shows how concepts are connected to everyday life (e.g., **Science in Context**).

- Sections that show how the six main concept areas are typically organized as curriculum topics (e.g., **Electrical Energy** is a typical topic within the main concept area of **Physical Science**).

- For each curriculum topic, readers are provided with an overview of important ideas that underpin the topic, information about how the topic is related to the **Alberta Elementary Science Program** (1996), a selection of website resources, and a list of typical activities in which children can participate

Additional Sources of Subject Matter Knowledge

Carin, A.A., Bass, J.E. & Contant, T.L. (2005). *Teaching Science as Inquiry (10th edition)*. NJ: Pearson.

Farrow, S. (1996). *The Really Useful Science Book: A Framework of Knowledge for Primary Teachers*. London: Falmer.

Fritzer, P. & Bristor, V.J. (2004). *Science Content for Elementary and Middle School Teachers*. Boston: Pearson.

Gega, P.C. & Peters, J.M. (1994). *Concepts and Experiences in Elementary SchoolScience (3rd edition)*. NJ: Merrill.

Hazen, R.M. & Trefil, J. (1990). *Science Matters – Achieving Scientific Literacy*. NY:Anchor Books.

Kent, A. & Ward, A. (1983). *The Usborne Book of Science: An Introduction to Biology, Physics and Chemistry*. London: Usborne. House.

Peters, J.M. & Gega, P.C. (2002). Science in Elementary Education (9th Edition). NJ: Pearson.

Trefil, J. (1992). *1001 Things Everyone Should Know About Science*. NY: Doubleday.

Physical Science

Physical science, which encompasses chemistry and physics, deals with the structure and properties of matter, energy, and forces and motion.

Everything on earth is made of matter that has structure and properties explained by the particle model of matter. The particle model of matter maintains that all matter is made of very small particles that are in constant motion. Understanding how these particles can be linked to or separated from each other to form different kinds of materials having different properties is important for understanding chemical change. Particle speed is influenced by adding or removing energy, and this helps explain physical changes such as change of state (e.g., change from solid to liquid, as when ice melts).

Energy is a property of many substances. Common K–7 energy topics include light, electrical, sound, heat, and magnetic energy. Energy can be transferred in many ways (e.g., heat energy can be transferred by convection) and changed to other forms of energy (e.g., electrical energy can be changed to heat energy), and these concepts can be used to connect various energy topics.

Forces (e.g., push, pull, and twist) can cause objects to speed up, slow down, or change direction (e.g., the force involved in kicking a soccer ball makes the ball speed up and change direction). Forces are usually explored through activities related to simple machines (e.g., levers and pulleys). Forces such as bending, twisting, and squashing can change the shape of objects. Gravity is a force that pulls us towards the center of the Earth.

In K–7 programs, physical science concepts are commonly organized under the following headings:

- **Properties of objects and materials** (e.g., materials have distinctive properties and matter and materials can be changed).
- **Light energy** (e.g., light is a form of energy and materials have different optical properties).
- **Magnetic energy** (e.g., magnetism is a form of energy and materials have different magnetic properties).
- **Sound energy** (e.g., sound is a form of energy and materials have different sound transmission properties).
- **Electrical energy** (e.g., electricity is a form of energy and electric currents carry energy).
- **Heat energy** (e.g., heat is a form of energy and materials have different heat properties).
- **Motion, forces, and simple machines** (e.g., forces cause objects to move or stay in position and simple machines help make work easier).

Science in Context 1: Physical Science at the Ballgame shows how physical science concepts are involved in a familiar context—baseball. As you can see, physical science concepts infuse our everyday lives. Studying this science area will help students understand familiar events and devices.

Science in Context 1

Physical Science at the Ballgame

Baseball is a context that can be used to understand how physical science concepts explain many aspects of our everyday lives. For instance, entering a stadium can involve walking up a ramp–an inclined plane. Walking up a ramp involves covering a longer distance than you would cover by simply stepping vertically to a higher level, but the inclined plane demands less effort from our bodies. Flags in the stadium are raised using fixed pulley systems whereby a downward pull on a rope results in the flag rising—an example of a change in the direction of force with no gain or loss in force or distance. Loudspeakers at the stadium convert sound energy into electrical energy and then back into sound energy, and stadium lights convert electrical energy into light energy and heat energy. When you sit down in your seat, gravity is the force that keeps you there. Should you be nearsighted, you might put on eyeglasses to see the action better. The lenses bend (refract) the light entering your eyes, allowing the light to focus on your retina and you to see the game with more clarity. The pop with ice that you drink are examples of a liquid and a solid. Note that the liquid has no shape of its own—to keep it together it must be contained within a cup. As the warm air and your warm hand add heat energy to the drink, the ice changes in state from a solid to a liquid. Munch on a hotdog and your body will change the chemical energy in the food into energy that keeps your body warm and moves your muscles.

A baseball bat is a lever that gives batters a mechanical advantage–an advantage that allows them to hit the ball long distances. Choking up on the bat reduces the length of the lever between the effort force (where the batter grips the bat) and the resistant force (where the ball contacts the bat), reducing the mechanical advantage but allowing for more precise control of the bat. Many batters try to contact the ball with the "sweet spot" on the bat, the point on the bat where contact makes the ball travel farthest. Bats vibrate when they come in contact with a baseball, and a node is a place on the bat where the vibrations are so small as to be hardly noticeable. The sweet spot is near a node, so hitting on the sweet spot makes the hit feel effortless and smooth because little energy is wasted on vibrations and more is available to launch the ball. Bat manufacturers spend much time and money experimenting with properties of materials and bat designs that will increase the size of the sweet spot.

If you are sitting in stadium seats located far from the batter's box, you might notice that after the batter swings there is a delay in hearing the crack of the bat. The sound of the bat striking the ball has traveled slower to your ears than the light reflecting off the batter has traveled to your eyes. When the next batter takes his position at the plate, the pitcher raises the ball in his glove, exerting a force over a distance (he does some work!). As the ball sits in the pitcher's glove, the ball has stored potential energy. More potential energy is added to the ball during the pitcher's windup. As the pitcher releases the ball towards the batter, the potential energy changes to kinetic energy (energy of motion). The moving ball and the moving bat both carry a lot of energy, and as the bat hits the ball, the bat transfers kinetic energy to the ball. Hitting the sweet spot will transfer a lot of energy, increasing the chance of a home run.

At the end of the game, the fireworks display features chemical energy being converted into the energy of light, sound, heat, and motion. As you drive home, the engine of your car converts chemical energy into heat energy that eventually results in motion down the highway.

Properties of Objects and Materials

Objects and materials have distinctive properties. These properties allow them to be distinguished from one another (e.g., size, weight, conductivity, texture, buoyancy, strength, hardness, solubility, boiling point, absorbency and density). Properties of materials may be used to separate a mixture (e.g., to separate sand from sugar, oil from water, and iron filings from sand). Heat may be transferred to or from or through different materials at different rates, from hot to cold (e.g., by conduction, radiation convection).

Matter and materials can also be changed. Some changes made to matter are reversible and some are not (e.g., a change of state is reversible, but a chemical change caused by combustion is not). Some materials can change shape or size without changing their properties (e.g., cutting wood into pieces doesn't change the properties of the wood). Most matter exists as a solid, liquid or gas. Matter can change in state with the addition or removal of energy (e.g., water can exist as a solid [ice], as a liquid, and as a gas [vapor]). Changes of state can be explained using the particle model of matter.

Website Resources

http://www.spacesciencegroup.nsula.edu
This website provides background information on the properties of matter and includes information about mass, volume, weight, density, states of matter, mixtures, elements, and compounds.

http://www.si.edu/nsrc/stcms.pmatter.htm
This website features information about the properties of matter and internet links to good websites that explain floating and sinking, density, mixtures, phases, compounds, elements, melting, and dissolving.

Links to Alberta Elementary Science Program

Creating Colour (Grade 1); *Exploring Liquids* (Grade 2); *Magnetism* (Grade 2); *Hot and Cold Temperature* (Grade 2); *Building with a Variety of Materials* (Grade 3); *Weather Watch* (Grade 5); *Electricity and Magnetism* (Grade 5); *Classroom Chemistry (Grade 5); Air and Aerodynamics* (Grade 6); *Evidence and Investigations* (Grade 6)

Typical Activities for Children 1
Properties of Objects and Materials

Concept:
Objects and Materials Have Distinctive Properties

- Using the senses to identify, describe, and classify materials and objects.

- Exploring the mechanical properties (e.g., hardness, elasticity, buoyancy, and density), thermal properties (e.g., how well or how poorly a material conducts heat, and at what temperature does the material boil), and optical properties (e.g., transparency, translucency, and opacity) of various materials and objects. Classifying materials according to these properties.

- Identifying materials that would be best for making common consumer products (e.g., waterproof coats and coffee cups).

- Exploring different states of matter (e.g., solid, liquid, and gas) and explaining these states using the particle model of matter.

- Exploring the properties of air (e.g., air has mass, occupies volume, is made of different gases, exerts pressure, and can be used to lift something heavy) and how these properties are related to flight (e.g., the flight of birds, kites, paper airplanes, and hot air balloons).

- Exploring the properties of various liquids (e.g., drop shape, color, ease of flow, tendency to bead, and interactions with other liquid and solid materials).

Concept:
Matter and Materials Can Be Changed

- Investigating the different states of water and the influence of adding or removing heat energy (e.g., evaporation, condensation, melting, and freezing).

- Exploring the differences and relationships among elements, compounds, and mixtures (e.g., liquid in liquid, liquid in solid, solid in solid, and solid in gas).

- Investigating reversible and irreversible changes (e.g., changes involved in heating water versus changes involved in heating cake batter or clay).

- Exploring physical changes where the material remains the same (e.g., mechanical changes, changes of state, physical mixing of substances, and expansion and contraction of metals).

- Exploring chemical changes where the change results in a new substance or substances being formed (e.g., burning a candle, cooking food, and rusting iron).

- Investigating how gas can be compressed (e.g., in a balloon).

- Investigating interactions between materials that result in the production of gas (e.g., adding baking soda to vinegar, adding Alka-Seltzer to water, and adding yeast to warm sugar water).

Light Energy

The sun is the earth's primary source of energy (heat and light). The sun's energy arrives as light with a range of wavelengths (e.g., visible light and ultraviolet light). Light travels in straight lines in all directions away from a source. Some objects emit their own light while other objects require an external light source to be seen (e.g., a light bulb versus a table). Light may be generated from or changed to other forms of energy (e.g., heat energy can make an object glow [emit light]; light energy can be changed into electrical or heat energy).

Some materials allow light to pass through (e.g., plastic wrap and lenses) while other objects reflect light (e.g., mirrors). White light can be separated into colors (e.g., in rainbows, with light filters, and by prisms). When objects block light, they cast a shadow (e.g., wood blocks). Light reflected from or emitted by an object must enter the eye for the object to be seen.

Website Resources

http://www.glenbrook.K12.il.us/gbssci/phys.class/light/lighttoc.html

This website provides background information on light waves, color, and vision.

http://www.geocities.com/Heartland/7134/Shadow/groundhog.htm

On this website you can learn about shadows, groundhogs, hibernation, and sundials.

http://www.geocities.com/Athens/Academy/6360/light.html

This website provides a list of concepts related to lights, mirrors, lenses, refraction, prisms, and wavelengths.

http://www.canteach.ca/links/linkright.html

This website contains great links to websites on light, rainbows, optics, and activities.

http://www.canteach.ca/links/linksolar.html

This website contains links to other websites about solar energy and science information about the sun.

Links to Alberta Elementary Science Program

Seasonal Changes (Grade 1); *Light and Shadows* (Grade 4), *Weather Watch* (Grade 5); *Sky Science* (Grade 6)

Typical Activities for Children 2: Light Energy

Concept:

Light Is a Form of Energy

Typical activities:

- Identifying different sources of light such as the sun, flames, lights, and materials that glow (e.g., luminescent materials).
- Distinguishing between objects that emit their own light and those that require an external light source to be seen (e.g., a firefly versus a mosquito).
- Exploring devices such as solar panels to understand how light can be changed to other forms of energy.
- Investigating how light travels in straight lines by trying to shine a flashlight beam through small pinholes and around corners.

Concept:

Materials Have Different Optical Properties

Typical activities:

- Distinguishing among transparent (e.g., glass and water), translucent (e.g., tissue paper and frosted glass) and opaque (e.g., wood and stone) materials.
- Exploring how opaque materials cast shadows. Drawing diagrams that show the position of the light source and the location, shape, and size of the shadow.
- Investigating how light travels outward from a source until blocked by some opaque material.
- Exploring changes in sun shadows during the day.
- Exploring how light is reflected from shiny surfaces such as mirrors and polished metals (e.g., measuring the angles of incidence and reflection).
- Investigating how light can be bent, or refracted (e.g., through prisms and lenses).
- Exploring how light can be broken into colors; identifying patterns in the colors produced by different prisms.
- Understanding that eyes can be damaged by bright lights (e.g., by looking into the sun).
- Using a light and a dark box to show that light needs to fall on objects and then reflect into our eyes in order for us to see the objects.
- Demonstrating how to use a variety of optical devices (e.g., camera, microscope and telescope).

Magnetic Energy

Magnetic energy can be generated from or changed to other forms of energy (e.g., power stations use magnetic energy to generate electricity; electromagnets use electricity to generate magnetic energy). Magnets have polarity (north and south poles). Magnets attract and repel each other (like poles repel, opposite poles attract).

Some materials are magnetic (e.g., iron, nickel, cobalt are attracted to magnets; copper and lead are not).

Website Resources

http://www.canteach.ca/links/linkmagnetism.html

This website contains links to websites on magnets, magnetism, electromagnets, and related lesson plans.

http://wwwistp.gsfc.nasa.gov/Education/lmagnet.html

This website features information on the history of magnets, the magnetosphere, how magnets work, and magnetic fields.

Links to Alberta Elementary Science Program

Magnetism (Grade 2); *Electricity and Magnetism* (Grade 5)

Typical Activities for Children 3: Magnetic Energy

Concept:
Magnetism Is a Form of Energy

Typical activities:

- Exploring how electricity can be used to create magnetism (e.g., using electromagnets).

- Demonstrating how a moving magnet can be used to generate electricity.

- Investigating evidence of magnetic fields around magnets and around wires carrying current (e.g., using iron filings, magnets, and compasses to show evidence of magnetic fields).

- Exploring how opposite poles attract and like poles repel (e.g., identifying the location of poles on bar magnets and horseshoe magnets).

- Investigating the direction in which a freely suspended magnet will point.

Concept:
Materials Have Different Magnetic Properties

Typical activities:

- Classifying materials as magnetic and nonmagnetic.

- Investigating how to make temporary magnets (e.g., by stroking a sewing needle with a magnet or inducing magnetism with an electric current).

Sound Energy

Sound is a form of energy and is produced by vibrations (e.g., vibrations caused by tapping on a table or plucking a guitar string). The pitch of a sound depends on the rate of vibrations (e.g., rapid vibrations result in a high pitch). The intensity of a sound depends on vibration size (e.g., small vibrations result in a soft sound). Ears have nerve endings designed to detect vibrations.

Sound vibrations travel differently through different solids, liquids and gases (e.g., Styrofoam, water and air). Sound vibrations bounce off some surfaces (e.g., echoes in a canyon).

Website Resources
http://www.geocities.com/Athens/Parthenon/6553/page11.html
This website contains ideas about how to teach about sound and sound waves, and how to build classroom musical instruments.

http://www.glenbrook.k12.il.US/gbssci/phys/Class/sound/soundtoc.html
This website contains background information on the nature of sound waves and properties of sound.

Links to Alberta Elementary Science Program
Senses (Grade 1); *Hearing and Sound* (Grade 3)

Typical Activities for Children 4: Sound Energy

Concept:
Sound Is a Form of Energy

Typical activities:

- Investigating a variety of ways of producing sound (e.g., striking objects together, blowing into a bottle, and plucking a stringed instrument).

- Investigating how sound is produced by vibrations.

- Exploring how pitch results from differences in the rate of vibration.

- Exploring how a musician can vary the pitch of a musical instrument (e.g., by working the slide in a slide trombone, covering or exposing holes in a clarinet, pressing on the valves of a trumpet, striking different size drums, and changing the thickness and tension of a string).

- Constructing musical instruments to demonstrate loudness and pitch.

- Describing how the human ear detects vibrations.

- Comparing the hearing range of humans to that of other animals (e.g., comparing humans to dogs).

- Describing how human hearing can be affected by exposure to loud noises (e.g., by misuse of personal stereo systems, lawnmowers, and chainsaws).

- Surveying noise levels in the school environment.

Concept:
Materials Have Different Sound Transmission Properties

Typical activities:

- Exploring how sound vibrations travel through different materials (e.g., solids, liquids, and gases) and that it travels in all directions.

- Constructing and evaluating ways to soundproof or to amplify sound (e.g., using sound-absorbing materials to construct a soundproofing device and evaluating how a megaphone amplifies sound).

Electrical Energy

Electrical energy may be generated from other forms of energy (e.g., solar panels generate electricity from light energy; batteries generate electricity from chemical energy). Electrical energy may be changed to other forms of energy (e.g., heat energy, by a toaster oven; light energy, by a light bulb; magnetic energy, by an electromagnet; sound energy, by speakers).

Electrical current occurs when a conductor forms a continuous loop with a source of electrical energy (e.g., in series and parallel circuits). Electrical current can be controlled (e.g., by fuses and switches). Some materials are conductors (e.g., copper and silver) and some are insulators (e.g., plastic and wood).

Website Resources

http://www.canteach.ca/links/linkgenelectric.html
This website features links to other websites about electricity, electrical utilities, and electrical facts for children.

http://www.sea.siemens.com/step/templates/lesson.m ason?motors:2:3:1
This website contains background information on AC motors and electrical energy.

http://www.amasci.com/ele-edu.html
This website contains a series of articles written by an electrical energy expert that address common misconceptions about electrical energy. Information about circuits, voltage, current electricity, and common electrical terminology is also included on the website.

Links to Alberta Elementary Science Program

Electricity and Magnetism (Grade 5); *Mechanisms Using Electricity* (Grade 5)

Typical Activities for Children 5: Electrical Energy

Concept:
Electricity Is a Form of Energy

Typical activities:
- Investigating evidence of magnetic fields around magnets and around current carrying wires (e.g., using iron filings, magnets, electrical currents, and compasses) to understand the connection between electricity and magnetism.

- Identifying common applications of electrical energy such as heating, lighting, communicating, and computing.

- Understanding how electrical energy can be generated from other forms of energy (e.g., generating electricity from chemical energy in batteries and from light energy in solar panels).

- Investigating renewable and nonrenewable sources of electricity (e.g., a hydroelectric power plant versus a coal-burning plant).

- Investigating how electricity has been generated over time (e.g., generating electricity from moving water, wind, and nuclear power).

- Investigating how electricity use affects regional natural resources (e.g., using coal reserves and damming rivers). Planning how to reduce personal electricity use (e.g., turning off lights when leaving a room).

Concept:
Electrical Currents Carry Energy

Typical activities:
- Classifying a variety of materials as electrical conductors or electrical insulators (e.g., copper wire versus a piece of wood). Classifying other materials as partial conductors (e.g., resistors).

- Exploring partial conductors of electricity (e.g., resistors) and the effect these have on an electrical circuit.

- Constructing circuits that operate lights, motors, and bells.

- Exploring how switches and fuses help control electrical circuits.

- Exploring series and parallel circuits–how to construct them, how to add lights to them, and how to compare them.

- Drawing and interpreting circuit diagrams (e.g., diagrams that include symbols for resistors, lights, motors, switches and power sources).

Heat Energy

The sun is the earth's primary source of energy (heat and light). Heat energy can be changed into other forms of energy (e.g., light). Temperature is a measure of heat energy and is measured in degrees (e.g., degrees Celsius and Fahrenheit). Heat energy is the total amount of thermal energy in a given amount of material (e.g., the total molecular movement in a bathtub of warm water [heat] is greater than the total molecular movement in a match flame [heat]).

Heat can be transferred between objects and materials. Heat may be transferred to or from or through different materials, at different rates, from hot to cold (e.g., by conduction, convection and radiation). Heat transfer between materials can be slowed (e.g., by insulation). Heat flows from warmer objects to cooler ones, until both reach the same temperature. Adding heat can change the state of materials (e.g., heating water to make it boil changes its state from liquid to gas). Removing heat can change the state of materials (e.g., cooling water can change its state from liquid to solid). Many materials change volume when heated or cooled (e.g., heating air makes it expand, as in a hot air balloon).

Website Resources

http://www.schoolforchampions.com/science/heat.htm
This website contains background information on heat, molecular theory, specific heat, and the ways in which heat influences matter.

http://id.mind.net/~zona/index.html
On this website you can search the physics area for information about the differences between heat and temperature.

Links to Alberta Elementary Science Program

Seasonal Changes (Grade 1); *Exploring Liquids* (Grade 2); *Hot and Cold Temperature* (Grade 2); *Plant Growth and Changes* (Grade 4); *Light and Shadows* (Grade 4); *Weather Watch* (Grade 5); *Flight* (Grade 6)

Typical Activities for Children 6: Heat Energy

Concept:
Heat Is a Form of Energy
Typical activities:

- Investigating how to measure temperature in degrees using a thermometer (e.g., degrees Celsius).

- Explaining temperature using the idea of kinetic energy and the particle model of matter.

- Contrasting the heat energy associated with different amounts of materials. Exploring how different surfaces absorb radiant heat (e.g., contrasting the heat absorption properties of a concrete sidewalk versus a grassy area).

- Understanding that human body temperature is relatively constant (e.g., a fever signals a change in health).

- Understanding that the earth's primary heat source is the sun (e.g., using solar cookers to illustrate solar energy).

- Investigating how buildings are heated (e.g., school building, office buildings, and houses).

Concept:
Materials Have Different Heat Properties
Typical activities:

- Exploring how heating and cooling can change a material or object (e.g., burning, freezing, and melting materials and objects).

- Investigating how insulation keeps things hot or cold (e.g., using house insulation, vacuum flasks, and fur and feathers to keep things warm; using refrigerators, coolers, and vacuum flasks to keep things cold).

- Exploring how heat energy can be transferred by conduction (the transfer of heat energy through a solid material), convection (the transfer of heat energy through a heated fluid such as air or water), and radiation (the transfer of heat energy by means of electromagnetic waves without the necessity of a material medium).

- Exploring how convection currents in fluids support the particle model of matter.

- Identifying how heat transfer principles are used to design everyday objects (e.g., homes, protective clothing, solar barbecues, oven mitts, refrigerators, and radiators).

- Exploring how heat flows from warmer objects to cooler ones (e.g., mixing together water of different temperatures and measuring the final temperature, and observing convection currents in fluids).

- Investigating the heating and cooling of water (e.g., measuring volume changes and observing changes of state).

A Practical Example of Physical Science Concepts Related to Matter and Heat Energy: Adding Salt to Ice

Related Contexts

When energy is removed from a liquid, the liquid cools and can become a solid. (e.g., water turning to ice or liquid flavored cream turning into ice cream). In the case of ice cream, as the salt ice mixture surrounding the cream container begins to melt, heat energy from the cream mixture helps 'power' this physical change from solid salt ice to liquid salt water. The result is that the cream loses energy and changes from a liquid to solid ice cream.

When liquid evaporates (e.g., rubbing alcohol evaporating from your arm), it uses heat energy usually from materials around it (e.g., your arm and the warm air in the room).

When a solid melts (e.g., ice melting into liquid water) energy is required often in the form of heat.

Adding energy to a substance or removing energy from a substance can cause changes to the substance (e.g., the substance may melt, freeze, evaporate or condense).

Important Ideas When Adding Salt to Ice

When salt is added to ice, there is no longer just ice in the container. Instead, you have 'salt ice' which has a different and much lower freezing point than ice. You may already know that different liquids have different freezing points from life experiences involving putting various alcoholic drinks into freezer compartments.

On a winter day in Edmonton, you have to wait until the temperature is near 0 C before ice on the roads begins to melt. However, if you spread some salt onto the ice, you only have to wait until it is around –15 C and it will melt! This is a great boon to drivers trying to negotiate icy streets. You can see this same phenomenon when working in the class____ ____ salt. Children ____ salt ic____ ____ is reg____ ____ere doe___ ___ energy ___ from in order to change solid ice with salt into liquid saltwater? Primarily the energy comes from the air around the salt ice. Remember that even on a cold winter day of –15 C, there is still enough heat energy in the air to result in melting salty streets!

Motion, Forces and Simple Machines

Forces can hold objects in position (e.g., gravity). Forces can also cause objects to move (e.g., push, pull and twist). To stop an object from moving, a force has to be applied (e.g., friction). The motion of an object can be described by its position, direction of motion and speed. Work is done when a force moves an object through a distance. Unbalanced forces cause changes in the speed or direction of an object's motion. Objects in motion that are not subjected to forces will continue to move at a constant speed and in a straight line.

Simple machines are part of everyday life (e.g., levers, wheels and axles, pulleys, inclined planes, wedges, and screws). There are three ways in which simple machines make work easier. Some simple machines provide an advantage in force by multiplying force (e.g., some levers). Some simple machines provide an advantage in distance (and speed) by multiplying distance (e.g., some gears). Some simple machines help to change the direction of a force (e.g., some pulleys and some gears). Simple machines can provide an advantage in force or an advantage in distance, but not both at the same time. An advantage in force is accompanied by a loss in distance, and an advantage in distance is accompanied by a loss in force.

Website Resources

http://www.glenbrook.k12.il.us/gbssci/phys/Class/energy/energtoc.html
This website provides background information on potential, kinetic, and mechanical energy, and power and work.

http://www.si.edu/nsrc/stems/energy.htm
This website features background information on energy, machines and motions, and good Internet links to sites dealing with these same topics.

http://www.canteach.ca/links/linksimplemachine.html
This website features links to websites about simple machines and motion energy.

Links to Alberta Elementary Science Program

Buoyancy and Boats (Grade 2); *Wheels and Levers* (Grade 4); *Building Devices and Vehicles That Move* (Grade 4); *Mechanisms Using Electricity* (Grade 5); *Air and Aerodynamics* (Grade 6); *Flight* (Grade 6)

Typical Activities for Children 7: Motion, Forces and Simple Machines

Concept:

Forces Cause Objects to Move or Hold Them in Position

Typical activities:

- Investigating how gravity is an attractive force between bodies as a result of their mass (e.g., releasing balls from heights and watching them drop towards earth).

- Investigating how to use forces to power or propel objects (e.g., pushing and pulling objects; powering objects using cranking mechanisms, moving water, rubber bands, springs, and moving air).

- Selecting and using tools to measure force (e.g., rubber bands and spring scales).

- Investigating how to change an object's direction and apply control mechanisms.

- Measuring and describing an object's position, direction of motion, and speed.

- Understanding that the motion of an object continues until some force is applied (e.g., friction)

Concept:

Simple Machines Help Make Work Easier

Typical activities:

- Investigating simple machines that are part of everyday life (e.g., screws, wedges, levers, wheels and axles, pulleys, inclined planes, and wheels and rollers).

- Describing how simple machines have been used for different applications over time.

- Exploring ways in which a lever can be used to create a large force from a small force (e.g., using a crowbar and car jack).

- Comparing the force needed to lift things manually to the force needed to lift the same object using a simple machine. Defining fulcrum, resistance force, and effort force.

- Exploring ways in which a lever can be used to create a large movement from a small movement (e.g., with a rake, baseball bat, and fishing rod).

- Exploring how changes in the size of a lever or the position of the fulcrum will affect the movement and forces involved.

- Exploring ways in which gears can be connected to transfer force, motion, and direction.

- Exploring ways in which the motion of objects is affected by rollers and the diameter of the roller.

- Exploring wheels and axles and how the size of each is connected to force (e.g., exploring faucets lacking handles or doorknob assemblies lacking doorknobs).

- Exploring pulleys, different combinations of single and multiple pulley systems, and how using pulleys can result in a gain in distance or force..

Life Science

Life science deals with the structure, growth, and interactions of living things with each other (e.g., interactions between plants and animals, animals and animals, and plants and microorganisms) and with the environment. Life science includes fields of study such as biology, cell biology, microbiology, biochemistry, ecology, zoology, botany, and genetics. When you consider the range of scientific and technological issues currently being debated (e.g., debates about cloning, stem cell research, population growth, preservation of wilderness areas, and the reintroduction of animal populations into areas where they once lived), you can see that many of these issues require an understanding of concepts associated with life science.

In K–7 programs, life science concepts are commonly organized under the following headings:

- **Meeting basic needs and maintaining a healthy body** (e.g., many living systems are made up of cells, tissues, and organs).

- **The needs and characteristics of living things** (e.g., organisms have basic needs, and many organisms respond to seasonal changes).

- **Plant and animal life cycles and growth** (e.g., life cycles are different for different organisms, and heredity involves passing traits from one generation to another).

- **Habitats and communities** (e.g., living things are affected by the nonliving features of their environments).

- **Diversity of life** (e.g., biological evolution accounts for the diversity of species over time, and living things have features that enable them to meet their needs).

Science in Context 2: Life Science in the Garden shows how life science concepts are involved in a familiar context—gardening. Studying this science area will help students understand familiar observations and events.

Part C

Science in Context 2

Life Science in the Garden

Gardens are a context that can be used to understand how life science concepts help explain many of the characteristics of living things and how they relate to each other in their environments. For instance, all living things in the garden, whether they are plants, animals, or microorganisms, are made of cells (or just one cell) that contain hereditary information important to reproduction. In most multi-cellular living things, cells are organized into organs and organs into systems. A gardener's immune system may identify the pollen released by flowers as an allergen and react with itchy eyes, sneezing, and a runny nose.

Living things depend on nonliving features of the environment to sustain life. For example, plants in your garden need sunlight (some plants thrive in full sunlight while others need some shade), space (more space leads to less competition for sun and nutrients), water (to dissolve and move nutrients), and air (plants use carbon dioxide from the air and release oxygen into the air). When you select plants for your garden, you keep these requirements in mind (e.g., by selecting *Hosta* plants for shady areas and sage for sunny areas with dry conditions). You might plan ahead for your garden by planting seeds in indoor trays; the seedlings could then be transplanted into your garden when the weather warms up. In this case, you would try to reproduce nonliving features of the environment that enhance seed germination and growth, by watering (providing sufficient water to help break down the seed coat) and by providing light (using grow lights that emit red and blue light), space (seeding sparingly), and air (using fans to circulate the air).

Living things also depend on other living things to sustain life. Birds such as robins, sparrows, and warblers may visit your garden to eat animals such as mosquitoes, beetles, and earthworms, and plant parts such as seeds, berries, and nuts–illustrating the idea of food chains. In turn, some plants depend on animals to disperse their seeds and enrich and aerate the soil.

People depend on plants to enhance and sustain life. Essential oils found in herbs such as parsley and basil help flavor foods, and some flowers, such as nasturtiums, can be added to salads. Vegetables and fruits add fiber and nutrients to our diet. Thyme contains a natural fungicide (thymol) that is a common ingredient in cough syrup, toothpaste, and mouthwash.

All living things have a life cycle that involves some form of reproduction. For instance, some plants in the garden (e.g., beans) grow from seeds, resulting in genetically variable populations. If you use vegetative propagation (e.g., using cuttings to grow geraniums), the resulting plants will be genetically identical. Either way, the young plants will grow into mature plants that can then be used to propagate the next generation. Insects in your garden change from larvae to adults through a process of metamorphosis that varies among species. Adult insects mate and the females lay eggs, and the cycle repeats.

Plants and animals have developed life cycles that are in synch with seasonal changes and environmental conditions. Animals such as birds and insects tend to either have or raise their young in spring to give the young time to grow, mature, and sometimes reproduce prior to colder seasons. For instance, mosquitoes hatch in the spring as nymphs, and then grow into flying adults, mate, and leave viable eggs prior to winter. Water is critical in the mosquito life cycle, so gardeners drain and clean artificial ponds during the off-season in order to avoid breeding mosquitoes.

Some plants (annuals) adapt to cold or dry climates by growing, maturing, reproducing, and dying in one growing season. Other plants (perennials) have a lifespan of many years. They adapt to severe environmental conditions by slowing or stopping growth, slowing down cellular processes, shedding leaves, or storing food in roots, tubers, and bulbs. You can design flowerbeds to take advantage of these different life cycles. For instance, to ensure lots of summer flower color, you can use annuals that have to grow, mature, and flower during that season. You can also use plants that flower at different times (such as spring or late summer) to ensure that you always have a colorful display.

Despite your best efforts, plants sometimes fail to thrive. Small animals such as aphids (on roses and peonies), slugs, and spider mites (on spruce trees) can stress or kill a plant. Microorganisms such as fungi (e.g., rusts, powdery mildew, Dutch elm disease, root rot) and viruses (e.g., tobacco mosaic virus) can also have a negative impact on plant health–illustrating the interdependence of plants and other living things.

After harvest, you collect dying plant material and either compost it or dig it into the soil to improve soil conditions. Plant matter adds to the organic content of the soil, improves the friability of the soil, and helps replenish nutrients. Plant matter stored in compost bins or dug into the soil is primarily broken down by worms and bacteria. These living things digest and excrete or otherwise decompose plant material. Either way, the plant material becomes part of a food chain.

In the end, a garden is a combination of science, art, history, and hope. Science concepts are used to inform the garden's design and artistry; the garden's history is expressed in the soil, trees, shrubs, and perennials; and the very act of planting and caring for living things is a symbol of hope for the future.

Meeting Basic Needs and Maintaining a Healthy Body

Living systems have a number of levels of organization (e.g., cells, organ, and tissues). All organisms are composed of cells. All cells carry out functions needed to sustain life (e.g., growth and division). Specialized cells carry out special functions needed to sustain life (e.g., blood cells). Humans have a number of systems that carry out different functions (e.g., digestion, respiration, movement, and response to stimuli). Skeletal, muscular, and nervous systems work together to produce movement. Systems comprise a number of major organs (e.g., digestive system comprises stomach, liver and intestines). Body systems help humans and other animals to grow, reproduce and to meet their basic needs. Human bodies have a variety of defenses against invasion (e.g., tears, saliva, and skin). To be healthy, bodies require nutritional and other requirements (e.g., food and exercise).

Website Resources

http://www.canteach.ca/links/linkbodysystems.html
This website links to other websites on all major human body systems (e.g., nervous, circulatory, respiratory, etc.).

http://www.enchantedlearning.com/subjects/anatomy/titlepage.shtml
This website contains information and activities about animal cell anatomy, the brain, ear, digestive system, eye, face, heart, skeleton, neurons, skin, tongue, and teeth.

http://users.rcn.com/jkimball.ma.ultranet/BiologyPages/P/PlantCell.html
This website features information about plant and animal cells.

http://www.eurekascience.com/ICanDoThat/plant_cells.htm
This website tells the story of cells and their constituents.

Links to Alberta Elementary Science Program

This topic is currently only found in the *Common Framework of Science Learning Outcomes* (1997). In Alberta, some ideas related to this topic can be found in the Elementary Health Program.

Typical Activities for Children 8: Meeting Basic Needs and Maintaining a Healthy Body

Concept:

Living Systems Have Levels of Organization

Typical activities:

- Understanding that living things have levels of organization that help them carry out processes needed to sustain and renew life (e.g., molecules, cells, tissues, organs, and organ systems).

- Investigating the human systems that carry out different functions (e.g., digestion, cardiovascular circulation, movement, and reproduction).

- Investigating the organs that make up different human systems (e.g., the digestive system comprises the stomach, liver, intestines, and other organs).

- Investigating how human bodies defend against microbial invasion (e.g., with tears, saliva, skin, nasal hairs, stomach secretions and mucus).

Concept:

Humans have nutritional and other requirements for health.

- Exploring nutrition and exercise requirements of a healthy lifestyle (e.g., describing a healthy diet using the Canada Food Guide and the importance of daily physical activity).

Needs and Characteristics of Living Things

Living things have basic needs, making them distinct from nonliving things (e.g., need for air, water and food). Living things live in environments where their needs are met. Plant parts undergo seasonal changes to meet their needs (e.g., seeds lie dormant and roots store food). Animals also respond to seasonal changes (e.g., hibernation, coat color protection and fat storage).

Living things have features that enable them to meet their needs (e.g., roots absorb water, eyes collect visual information, and leaves make food). Plants have features that enable them to meet their needs in special places (e.g., desert plants have prickles). Animals have features that enable them to meet their needs in special places (e.g., some aquatic animals have gills and others have webbed feet). Microorganisms have features that enable them to meet their needs in special places (e.g., cilia enable movement). Behavior evolves through adaptation to the environment (e.g., animals have evolved keen senses that help them avoid predators).

Website Resources

http://www.enchantedlearning.com/subjects/mammals
This website contains information about mammals, their diets, classification, and evolution. A geologic time chart is also included to aid your interpretation of changes to mammal over time.

http://www.enchantedlearning.com/subjects/birds
This website features information about birds, feathers, flying, diet, reproduction, migration, and classification.

Links to the Alberta Elementary Science Program

Small Crawling and Flying Animals (Grade 2); *Animal Life Cycles* (Grade 3); *Plant Growth and Changes* (Grade 4); *Wetland Ecosystems* (Grade 5); *Trees and Forests* (Grade 6)

Typical Activities for Children 9: Needs and Characteristics of Living Things

Concept:
Living Things Have Basic Needs

Typical activities:

- Classifying things as living or nonliving (e.g., living things move, reproduce, respond to stimuli, grow, feed, excrete, and respire).

- Investigating the different environments in which living things live (e.g., deserts, forests, oceans, and lakes).

- Exploring how plants undergo seasonal changes to meet their needs (e.g., seeds lie dormant and roots store food).

- Exploring how animals undergo seasonal changes to meet their needs (e.g., migration, hibernation, coat color protection, and fat storage).

- Exploring how living things have anatomical features that enable them to meet their needs (e.g., roots, eyes, leaves, claws, teeth, and ears).

- Investigating how plants, animals, and microorganisms have features that allow them to sustain life in special places (e.g., in deserts, oceans, ponds, high elevations, deep shade, intertidal zones, and saline soil).

- Exploring different ways in which behavior evolves through adaptation to the environment (e.g., monkeys have evolved special calls that warn about predators).

Plant and Animal Life Cycles and Growth

Living things have life cycles. Animal life cycles can be classified according to similarities and differences (e.g., life cycles of insects, amphibians, and reptiles are similar in some ways, different in others). Plant life cycles can be classified according to similarities and differences (e.g., conifers and deciduous trees have different life cycles). Life cycles are different for different organisms (e.g., different lengths and different stages).

Reproduction is a characteristic of all living systems (e.g., sexual and asexual reproduction). Living things have traits that change and traits that remain constant (e.g., number of arms versus height and weight). Heredity involves passing traits from one generation to another. Hereditary information is located in genes found in chromosomes inside cells.

Offspring tend to resemble their parents. Plant offspring are much like their parent(s) but can differ in some ways (e.g., different colored flowers).

Animal offspring generally look like their parent(s) but can differ in some ways (e.g., different size).

Web Site Resources

http://www.yesnet.yk.ca/schools/jackhulland/project s/butterflies/
This website designed by children features the metamorphosis of a painted lady butterfly.

Links to the Alberta Elementary Science Program

Small Crawling and Flying Animals (Grade 2); *Animal Life Cycles* (Grade 3); *Plant Growth and Changes* (Grade 4); *Wetland Ecosystems* (Grade 5); *Trees and Forests* (Grade 6)

Typical Activities for Children 10: Plant and Animal Life Cycles and Growth

Concept:
Living Things Have Life Cycles

Typical activities:

- Exploring the life cycles of common plants and animals (e.g., mealworms, guppies, butterflies, and the Wisconsin fast plant [Brassica rapa]).

- Investigating and classifying plant life cycles according to similarities and differences (e.g., seed-producing plants have a life cycle that includes seed germination, seedlings, flowering, pollination, seed and fruit development, and seed germination again).

- Investigating and classifying animal life cycles according to similarities and differences (e.g., some insects undergo a complete metamorphosis that includes an egg, larva, pupa, and adult, whereas other insects do not).

Concept:
Living Things Can Reproduce

Typical activities:

- Understanding that reproduction is a characteristic of living systems (e.g., asexual reproduction such as budding in yeast cells and spore formation in ferns; vegetative reproduction in potatoes and onions; sexual reproduction in mammals, birds, and flowering plants).

- Classifying traits that remain constant and those that change due to genetic variation (e.g., number of legs versus eye color and height).

- Understanding that, in sexual reproduction, genetic variation arises from the mixing of parental chromosomes (e.g., genes are found in chromosomes inside cells and each parent contributes half the offspring's chromosomes).

- Offspring resemble their parents (e.g., cows have calves) but also can differ in some ways from the parents (e.g., calf coloring).

Habitats and Communities

Different kinds of plant and animal populations exist in various environments. Living things are affected by the nonliving features of their environment (e.g., climate, soil, and water availability). Living things cause changes to the environments in which they live (e.g., elephants uproot trees, algae affect pond oxygen levels, and plants help maintain soil and air quality). The behavior of living things is related to the environment (e.g., migration). Humans depend on their natural and constructed environments.

Individuals of a species occur in populations. A population consists of the individual members of a species that occur together in a given time and place (e.g., coyotes in a protected area and dandelions in a lawn). Populations can be categorized by the functions they serve in an ecosystem (e.g., producer, consumer, and decomposer). Which populations an ecosystem can support depends on available resources and abiotic factors (e.g., light, water, and temperature).

Population size reflects the interdependency between plants and animals (e.g., as shown by food chains and food webs). Animals depend on plants (e.g., for food, shelter, and medicine). Plants benefit from animals (e.g., from seed dispersal and soil enrichment). Population size can be affected by changes in local environmental conditions (e.g., fire, floods, and drought).

Energy and matter flow through ecosystems. The major source of energy for most ecosystems is the sun (heat and light). Energy flows through an ecosystem (e.g., in a food web). Matter is recycled in ecosystems through interactions among living things (e.g., among plants, animals, and microorganisms).

Extinction of species is common. Habitat loss and adaptive capability can affect population size and existence (e.g., populations can become endangered or even extinct).

Fossils show that living things change over time and many types of organisms have become extinct.

Website Resources

http://www.evergreen.ca/nativeplants/learn-more/natural-habitats.php
This website contains information about the types of natural habitat communities in Canada.

http://www.pc.gc.ca
The Parks Canada website features descriptions of Canada's natural parks and hot links to other related sites.

http://www.enchantedlearning.com/biomes
This website contains information about different biomes or habitats, characteristics of terrestrial biomes, and coral reefs, oceans, ponds, swamps, marshes, and the intertidal zone.

http://www.amnh.org/nationalcenter/Endangered/
This website features information about endangered animals, the causes of endangerment, and how human populations impact on other species.

Links to the Alberta Elementary Science Program

Needs of Plants and Animals (Grade 1); *Small Crawling and Flying Animals* (Grade 2); *Animal Life Cycles* (Grade 3); *Plant Growth and Changes* (Grade 4); *Wetland Ecosystems* (Grade 5); *Trees and Forests* (Grade 6)

Typical Activities for Children 11: Habitats and Communities

Concept:
Different Kinds of Plant and Animal Populations Exist in Various Environments

Typical activities:

- Exploring how plants and animals are affected by nonliving features of their environment (e.g., availability of food, warmth, light, water, safe places, and soil).

- Exploring interactions between biotic and abiotic factors in an ecosystem (e.g., interactions between plants and available water).

- Investigating how plants and animals cause changes to the environments in which they live (e.g., how overpopulation can lead to environmental degradation).

- Investigating how humans depend on natural (e.g., forests and oceans) and constructed (e.g., houses) environments and how humans change those environments in environmentally beneficial or detrimental ways (e.g., removing foreign plant species may lead to native plant species repopulating an area, clear cutting forests may lead to erosion, dumping toxins into the ocean may lead to reduced fish populations, open pit mining may lead to erosion, urban sprawl can cover quality farmland, consuming large quantities of a single species can lead to endangerment or extinction, habitat loss can lead to endangerment or extinction).

Concept:
Individuals of a Species Occur in Populations

Typical activities:

- Investigating populations of plants and animals and how those populations interact within a habitat to form a community (e.g., plant populations and insect populations interacting in a lawn).

- Investigating how population size is related to abiotic factors (e.g., light, water, and temperature).

- Investigating how population size reflects the interdependency between plants and animals in food chains and food webs (e.g., animals may eat plants, and plants may benefit from animals dispersing their seeds).

- Identifying population trends in data collected from a simulation game that models the interdependency of plants and animals.

- Observing and classifying living things as producers (e.g., plants and some microorganisms that make their own food), consumers (e.g., herbivores and carnivores), and decomposers (e.g., bacteria, fungi, and small animals such as earthworms that live in soil and waste materials and dead organisms).

- Comparing the features of plants and animals that enable them to thrive in different places (e.g., climbing plants have tendrils and some birds have webbed feet)

Concept:
Energy and Matter Flow Through Ecosystems

Typical activities:

- Investigating how energy and matter are recycled through interactions within ecosystems (e.g., plants carry out photosynthesis, animals consume plants and other animals, and microorganisms decompose organic matter).

- Constructing a chart that shows the flow of energy in a food web in a local context (e.g., food webs and chains observed in the schoolyard).

- Investigating how matter is recycled in an ecosystem through interactions among plants, animals, fungi, and microorganisms.

Concept:
Extinction of a Species Is Common

Typical activities:

* Investigating examples of environmental conditions that may threaten animal and plant survival (e.g., climate change and habitat loss).

* Investigating examples of extinct animals (e.g., in the fossil record) and exploring theories of how they came to be extinct.

Diversity of Life

Organisms exhibit unity and diversity. All living things share a certain unity (e.g., they have cells and systems, perform chemical processes, have ancestry, and fill needs). Biological evolution accounts for the diversity of species over time.

Biological classification takes into account the diversity of life on Earth. Animals can be grouped according to common characteristics (e.g., vertebrates and invertebrates; mammals, birds, reptiles, amphibians, and fishes). Plants can be grouped according to common characteristics (e.g., conifers and deciduous trees).

Some living things cannot be seen with the naked eye (e.g., microorganisms). Microorganisms meet their basic needs for food water, air, and movement in many ways (e.g., through decomposing matter.

Website Resources

http://www.hhmi.org/coolscience/
This website invites curious kids to explore biology concepts.

http://www.canteach.ca/links/linkecology.html
This website provides links to other websites on composting, ecosystems, environmentalism, rainforest issues, recycling, and world wildlife issues.

http://www.enchanted learning.com/subjects/plants
This website contains an illustrated dictionary of plant terms and information about how to construct a dichotomous key.

Links to the Alberta Elementary Science Program

Needs of Plants and Animals (Grade 1); *Small Crawling and Flying Animals* (Grade 2); *Animal Life Cycles* (Grade 3); *Plant Growth and Changes* (Grade 4); *Wetland Ecosystems* (Grade 5); *Trees and Forests* (Grade 6)

Typical Activities for Children 12: Diversity of Life

Concept:
Organisms Exhibit Unity and Diversity

Typical activities:

* Investigating how living things share characteristics that are related to cell specialization (e.g., all life is based on combinations of organic and inorganic molecules, molecules are assembled into cells, groups of cells working together are called tissues, and tissues are grouped together in organs).

* Investigating how biological adaptation through evolution accounts for the diversity of species over time (e.g., adaptation can account for changes in structures, behavior, and reproductive success).

* Comparing the adaptations of closely related animals living in different parts of the world (e.g., different bear species).

Concept:
Some Living Things Cannot Be Seen With the Naked Eye

* Describing microorganisms in a pond community (e.g., rotifers).

* Describing ways in which microorganisms meet their basic needs (e.g., accessing oxygen dissolved in water).

Concept:
Living Things Can Be Classified

Typical activities:

* Classifying a variety of animals (e.g., mealworms, gerbils, guppies, and earthworms) based on observable characteristics (e.g., the characteristics of their limbs, teeth, and body covering; how they feed their young and what they eat; and the presence or absence of a backbone) as mammals, birds, fish, reptiles, amphibians, insects, and so on.

* Classifying common plants on the basis of their characteristics and uses (e.g., whether they bear seeds, have flowers, or have a certain leaf shape or bark color).

Earth and Space Science

Earth and space science allows students to develop a broad perspective on the **earth's materials** (e.g., rocks, soil, water, and atmospheric gases), **landforms** (e.g., features on the earth's surface resulting from constructive and destructive forces), **weather** (e.g., precipitation viewed as part of the water cycle), and **place in the solar system** (e.g., in relationship to the sun, moon, and other planets). Through these studies, students can see that earth exhibits physical properties and patterns of change, as does our solar system and the universe beyond it. Earth and space science includes fields of study such as geology, oceanography, hydrogeology, meteorology, and astronomy.

In K–7 programs, earth and space science concepts are commonly organized under the following headings:

- **Rocks, minerals, and erosion** (e.g., classifying rocks and minerals according to their properties, and exploring the properties of soil, water, and atmospheric gases).

- **Weather phenomena** (e.g., changes in the weather, seasonal changes).

- **The earth in the solar system** (e.g., the earth's relationship to other celestial bodies and changes in the length of day and night).

Science in Context 3: Earth and Space Science at the Campsite shows how earth and space science concepts are involved in a familiar context–camping. As you can see, earth and space science concepts infuse our everyday lives. Studying this science area will help students understand familiar observations and experiences.

Part C

Science in Context 3

Earth and Space Science at the Campsite

Camping is a context that can be used to understand how earth and space science concepts help us to understand the world around us. For instance, having reached a camping area in the mountains, we have to select a campsite and set up camp. Hammering in tent pegs can be difficult or easy depending on the ground at the campsite. Sparse, rocky soil presents a challenge, and pegs can easily pull out of sandy soil. A heavy clay soil can be difficult to penetrate, but the peg is usually held fast. Soil is formed over time by the breakdown of rocks and decomposition of organic matter, with wind, rain, streams, glaciers, and the local plant life all contributing to the type of soil at your campsite. One way to think about the soil and rocks at your campsite is as historical documents that contain a record of events in the earth's history. By studying soil and rocks, you can learn about the seas, rivers, winds, earthquakes, volcanoes, and passing glaciers that left their mark on the landscape.

After pitching your tent, you may find that the exertion has left you somewhat short of breath. This reaction is common at higher elevations, where the atmosphere contains less oxygen. Once you climb above about 5,500 meters (18,000 feet), there is only about half as much oxygen available to you as there is at sea level.

Going on a hike through a river valley near the campsite gives you a chance to view different landforms, rocks, and if you're lucky, fossils. The fact that you're in a river valley shows how water, and perhaps past glaciers, can change the landscape. As you look up at one of the surrounding cliffs, then allow your eyes to travel down the cliff to where you are standing near the river, you are looking back in time. The youngest layer (or profile) of soil and rock is near the top of the cliff. As you scan down the cliff, you see progressively older layers till you finally hit bedrock. Each layer tells a story of where winds blew or water or lava flowed. For example, if a layer contains fossil shells of sea creatures (usually found in sedimentary rock), you know that in the past the area was covered by ocean water. The presence of a layer of coal shows that the area once had a great deal of plant life (dead plant matter, subjected to the right conditions underground, can turn into coal). Processes such as the weathering, erosion, transport, and deposition of surface rock, and the melting of subsurface rock, help explain how over time layers can be formed and rocks can be transformed to other kinds of rock or can become soil.

Rocks in the river or near the river's edge likely have a smooth appearance. Over time, as water washes over rocks, sometimes tumbling them together, it polishes them to a smooth finish. As the rocks continue to wear down, they can become small enough for the river to move them great distances, sometimes forming beds of sand and gravel.

Returning to your campsite, you notice that shadows are lengthening, the air is beginning to cool, and storm clouds have gathered on the horizon. Shadows, which are caused by objects that block light from the sun, grow longer in late afternoon and early evening when the angle of the sun's rays is much lower in the sky. During the day, the sun heats the atmosphere and the earth's surface, adding energy to the weather system. Winds follow, caused by the unequal heating of various surfaces, and water evaporates as its molecules speed up and enter a gaseous state.

As you sit inside the tent, the walls of the tent begin to move from the winds of the approaching storm. As the wind increases, sometimes the tent appears to be rising off its moorings. These phenomena show that air has properties such as mass, weight, and the ability to exert pressure. The rain soon begins to pour down on the campsite, providing water for living things, sinking into the earth to circulate through the crust, eroding soil and rock, and filling rivers and aquifers.

After the storm, the clouds clear and the moon and stars appear in the night sky. Looking out at the moon (we really look out at the universe, not up–there is no up or down in astronomical space), you see the right hand side is lit up and the left side is dark. The sun, now below the earth's horizon, is illuminating the right side of the moon. Over the next few days, more and more of the moon will be illuminated until you can see a full moon in the sky. Then, as the moon continues to travel around the earth, the left side will appear illuminated, only to wane to a new moon. In the night sky, you can also see other lights (some brighter than others) that at first glance appear as random patterns. A pocket guide to the night sky shows that, given your campsite's position in the northern United States, you should be able to see the Big Dipper. Identifying the Big Dipper makes it easy to find Polaris (the North Star) and the constellation Cassiopeia (looks like a giant W in the sky). Most of the stars and constellations that you see appear in different positions at different times of the year, while others seem to come and go. This is due to the earth's yearly orbit around the sun, which allows us to gaze out at different areas of the universe.

As you ready yourself for sleep, you realize that time and change are two unifying ideas that recur when looking at the earth and the sky. Time and change also infuse your own storyline as you experience the physical, social, and personal changes that occur during your life.

Rocks, Minerals, and Erosion

Earth's materials include rocks, soil, water and atmospheric gases. The earth's crust is made of different kinds of rocks and minerals (e.g., igneous, metamorphic, and sedimentary rocks). Different kinds of rocks are formed in different ways (e.g., by pressure, heating, and cooling). Different kinds of rocks have different properties (e.g., color, texture, hardness, luster, and presence of carbonates). Rocks can be broken down in different ways (e.g., by wind, water, cooling and warming, and living organisms).

Breakdown of rock contributes to soil formation (e.g., formation of sand, silt, clay, pebbles). Different soils have different properties (e.g., color, proportions of clay, silt, sand, and plant material) and, therefore, different ability to support plant growth. Soils are often found in layers.

The earth is structured in layers: the outermost layer is the lithosphere (including the crust, continents, and plates), the middle layer is the mantle, and the inner layer is the dense, metallic core (mostly made of nickel and iron). Lithospheric plate movements shift the positions of the continents and cause earthquakes and volcanic eruptions. Landforms are the result of constructive and destructive forces (e.g., earthquakes and volcanic eruptions can construct new landforms, while weathering and erosion break down existing landforms). Certain cycles can change landforms (e.g., the rock cycle and the water cycle).

Water is a unique substance. Water is like other liquids in many ways (e.g., it acquires the shape of its container). Water has properties that distinguish it from other liquids (e.g., capillarity and density). Water is a great solvent (e.g., it dissolves many minerals and gases). Water is needed by all living things. Water circulates through the crust, water systems, and atmosphere in what is called the water cycle.

Earth's atmosphere is a mixture of gases (e.g., nitrogen, oxygen, and trace gases). Earth's atmosphere has different properties at different elevations (e.g., different amounts of oxygen). Global patterns of atmospheric movement influence the weather. Air occupies space, has mass, and exerts pressure (e.g., in tires).

Earth has a geological and biological history. Earth's processes were similar in the past (e.g., the water cycle and weathering). Fossils provide evidence of past plants, animals, and environments.

Website Resources

http://www.canteach.ca/links/linkgeology.html
This website provides links to other websites on geology and geological regions.

http://www.fi.edu/fellows/payton/rocks
On this website, children can find out about collecting and classifying rocks.

http://www.enchantedlearning.com/geology
This website contains good information and activities about the earth, soil, rocks and minerals, the water cycle, and volcanoes.

Links to the Alberta Elementary Science Program

Exploring Liquids (Grade 2); *Rocks and Minerals* (Grade 3); *Plant Growth and Changes* (Grade 4); *Weather Watch* (Grade 5); *Air and Aerodynamics* (Grade 6)

Typical Activities for Children 13: Rocks, Minerals, and Erosion

Concept:

Earth's Materials Include Rocks and Minerals, Soil, Water, and Atmospheric Gases

Typical activities:

• Investigating different properties of rocks and minerals, such as color, luster, texture, hardness, crystal shape, and the presence of carbonates.

• Classifying rocks and minerals based on their properties. Comparing descriptions of different rocks and minerals.

• Classifying rocks as igneous (formed by the cooling of molten magma), metamorphic (formed under heat and/or pressure), or sedimentary (formed by erosion, transport, and settling).

- Exploring the ways in which rocks break down to become soil (e.g., through the action of wind, water, cooling and warming, and living organisms). Demonstrating how rocks break down (e.g., by shaking soft rocks in a jar of water or striking rocks together).

- Exploring the various components of soil (e.g., sand, silt, clay, and organic material); using sieves to separate soil components or shaking a soil sample in a jar of water and then allowing the soil to settle into layers.

- Identifying ways to maintain the soil base required to support plant and animal life (e.g., using alternative farming methods such as zero tillage).

- Investigating layers of the earth by constructing models of the core, mantle and lithosphere.

- Understanding how earthquakes and volcanic eruptions are related to lithospheric plate movements (e.g., they happen where tectonic plates are in contact).

- Investigating how knowledge about earthquakes is related to the development of building specifications.

- Exploring the properties of water (e.g., density, capillarity, surface tension, interaction with materials such as oil and wax, and various states).

- Exploring how water affects the landscape (e.g., using an erosion activity and a variety of different soils).

- Exploring how heating and cooling energize the water cycle by demonstrating precipitation, transpiration, evaporation, and condensation.

- Exploring properties of air (e.g., air occupies space, has mass, exerts pressure, and behaves as a fluid).

- Investigating the mixture of gases that make up the earth's atmosphere (e.g., testing for the presence of oxygen and carbon dioxide).

Concept:

Earth Has a Geological and Biological History

Typical activities:

- Understanding that basic processes such as the water cycle, rock cycle, and oxygen cycle were similar in the past.

- Exploring fossils and understanding how they provide evidence of the past (e.g., evidence of climate, environments, life cycles, and food chains).

Weather Phenomena and the Earth in the Solar System

The sun is the earth's primary source of heat energy, which influences climate, weather, seasons, ocean currents, and the water cycle. Weather changes from day to day and across the seasons. All precipitation is water in different physical states (e.g., snow and rain). Water cycles from earth's surface to the atmosphere and to the surface again. (e.g., by evaporation and condensation). Moving air masses (whose motion is caused by energy derived from the sun) help determine weather. Weather can be measured (e.g., by temperature and wind direction).

Objects in the solar system are in regular and predictable motion. Objects in the sky have regular patterns of movement (e.g., the sun appears to move, and the moon goes through phases). Motion explains certain events (e.g., day, year, and phases of the moon). Seasons are a consequence of earth's movement around the sun and the tilt of the earth's axis. Some events occur at regular intervals of time (e.g., day length changes with the seasons, planets revolve around the sun, the moon goes through phases, and eclipses occur at predictable times).

Earth is positioned within a solar system. Our solar system includes ten planets, their moons, the sun, and other smaller objects such as asteroids and comets. (Recently, astronomers at Cal. Tech. have discovered a new planet larger than Pluto in the outer regions of our solar system). The sun is the central and largest body in our solar system. Knowledge of our solar system is continually changing (e.g., additional moons are discovered for some planets).

Gravity is an important force in our universe. Gravity keeps planets in orbit around the sun and governs motion in the solar system. Gravity is a force of attraction between bodies as a result of their mass (e.g., between the earth and moon, between the earth and people, between planets and the sun). Gravity between the earth and moon primarily explains tidal phenomena.

Website Resources

http://www.units.muohio.edu/dragonfly/snow/
On this website you can learn about ice and snow, and travel to Antarctica.

http://beakman.com/moon/moonstuff.html

On this website, Beakman and Jax explain why we see phases of the moon.

http://spaceplace.jpl.nasa.gov/index.shtml
This is NASA's site for children. The website contains space science in action and space facts. There is also good information for teachers too.

http://www.enchantedlearning.com/subjects/astronomy
This website contains good information and activities on the planets, the solar system, the sun, and the moon.

http://www.enchantedlearning.com/subjects/astronomy/planets/earth
Good information about the moon, the earth, earth's orbit, tilt, speed, and temperature.

http://www.canteach.ca/links/linkweather.html
This website features links to websites about tornadoes, hurricanes, clouds, rainbows, and the weather.

http://www.canteach.ca/links/linkspace.html
This website features links to websites about space science.

http://www.glenbrook.k12.il.us/gbssci/phys/Class/circles/circtoc.html
This website contains background information on universal gravitation, circular motion, and planetary and satellite motion.

Links to the Alberta Elementary Science Program

Seasonal Changes (Grade 1); *Light and Shadows* (Grade 4); *Weather Watch* (Grade 5); *Sky Science* (Grade 6)

Typical Activities for Children 14: Weather Phenomena and the Earth in the Solar System

Concept:
Many Factors Determine the Weather

Typical activities:

- Exploring patterns of air movement in indoor and outdoor environments.

- Investigating methods for measuring air temperature, wind speed, air pressure, relative humidity, and dew point using standard or student-constructed instruments (e.g., thermometers, barometers, and hygrometers).

- Measuring precipitation (e.g., snow and rain) at school and relating these measurements to local weather forecasting information.

- Classifying cloud types and relating these types to weather conditions (e.g., stratus and cumulonimbus).

- Understanding the difference between climate (long-term trends) and weather (shorter phenomena). Identifying seasonal patterns in atmospheric conditions using historical weather data.

- Exploring how heating and cooling energize the water cycle by demonstrating precipitation, transpiration, evaporation, and condensation.

- Exploring how heated fluids rise over cooler fluids and understanding that weather systems are generated from the unequal heating of the earth's surface.

- Understanding how wind happens and the relationship between wind speed and the rate of evaporation of surface water.

- Relating the transfer of energy from the sun to weather conditions.

Concept:
Objects in the Solar System Are in Regular and Predictable Motion

Typical activities:

- Constructing student-made models of the solar system (e.g., sun, planets, moons, and asteroid belt).

- Demonstrating that the apparent movement of objects in the night sky is regular and predictable (e.g., moon phases and changes in star patterns in the night sky).

- Constructing a sundial or shadow stick to show the apparent movement of the sun over the course of a day and the school year.

- Demonstrating the phases of the moon using student-made models. Predicting what variables affect the size of craters on the moon, using a flour and marble simulation.

- Exploring how seasonal changes in the length of the day and night are related to the angle of the sun above the horizon.

Concept:
The Earth Is Positioned Within the Universe

Typical activities:

- Exploring the relative position and motion of objects in space by constructing movable models showing relative distances.

- Building model constellations.

• Locating information about our evolving understanding of the universe (e.g., researching newspaper articles and website information related to the Hubble Space Telescope).

Concept:
Gravity Is an Important Force in the Universe

Typical activities:

• Investigating how gravity exerts a downward force on objects.

• Understanding that gravity is a force of attraction between objects with mass.

• Comparing the weight of an object on Earth to what it would weigh on the Moon; understanding the relationship of weight, gravity, and mass.

• Investigating the relationship among the moon, the earth, and the sun (e.g., by studying moon phases, eclipses, and tidal phenomena); making charts and drawings that illustrate this relationship.

• Describing how astronauts meet their basic needs in space.

Technological Structures and Devices

Studying technological structures and devices allows students to explore the **designed or manufactured world**. Students can design and build models of technological artifacts and devices. Students can study the constraints that impact on design and how technological solutions have trade-offs (e.g., vehicles can transport us at a faster rate but add to air pollution).

In K–7 programs, students can identify human wants and needs, design and build models and devices, study local and global examples of technology, consider relationships between science and technology, and think about the broader picture of how science and technology reflect social values. Concepts related to technological structures and devices are commonly organized under the following areas:

- **Designing and building technological structures** (e.g., containers, bridges and towers).
- **Designing and building devices that move** (e.g., vehicles that move in a variety of ways).

Science in Context 4: Technology at the Skating Rink shows how technology concepts are involved in a familiar context—a skating rink. As you can see, technology concepts infuse our everyday lives. Studying this area will help students understand the pervasive nature of technology and the need to think critically about technological solutions.

Part C

Science in Context 4

Technology at the Skating Rink

Going to a skating rink is a context that can be used to understand how technological concepts explain many aspects of our sporting lives. For instance, things at the skating rink are either natural or human made. Geological and biological natural materials include rocks, sand, clay, wood, cotton, and wool. These natural materials are then made into manufactured products such as hockey nets, benches, glass, concrete, skates, and clothing. In many cases, technologists had to develop knowledge of natural materials in order to design manufactured products that meet our needs.

Many rural skating rinks have an arched or barrel roof. Arched or barrel roofs are strong structures because the upward bend gives the roof a curvature that allows it to carry some weight in addition to its own dead load. Other rinks have flat roofs supported by ceiling trusses. Trusses add strength to the roof enabling it to safely support heavy snowfalls. Benches frequently have a triangular brace attaching the seat to the supports. The triangular braces increase the strength of the bench enabling it to support a greater load or number of skaters.

Children learning to skate frequently take a wider stance in order to prevent falls. A wider base than top increases stability much as it does in camera tripods. Holding onto a chair and pushing it around the rink also helps new skaters to increase their stability because the chair features a stable design.

Ceiling fans feature electric motors that are able to convert electricity to movement. The fan's moving shaft is attached to blades that turn as they circulate a ir throughout the rink. Switches allow people to control fan speed and direction. Turning the switch off interrupts the flow of electrical current stopping the fan blades.

Technological solutions, however, have trade-offs. Heaters at the skating rink may use nonrenewable energy sources. Incomplete gas combustion and coal-burning generating plants lead to air pollution. Heaters not serviced on a regular basis can lead to fires. Faulty pilot lights can result in gas explosions. As systems fail, heaters need to be repaired and replaced parts that cannot be recycled are discarded into landfill sites.

Technological solutions also operate under constraints. Designing and manufacturing skating rink heaters involved assessing the kinds of materials to use; their cost, durability, and thermal properties; and the overall aesthetics of the product. Consumers had to be convinced that the product was worth purchasing and would meet their needs. Technologists, therefore, had to balance creativity with practicality in their bid to profit from the sale of their products.

Technology infuses our everyday life, reflect our values, and in turn, influence us to value some things more than others. As teachers, we can help our students become critical consumers who ask themselves why they are purchasing a product and consider the outcomes of their decisions.

Designing and Building Technological Structures

Building strong and stable structures is a function of the materials used (e.g., paper versus wood), the way materials are joined together (e.g., with glue or by folding), and the overall design of the structure (e.g., low center of gravity versus high center of gravity).

The physical properties of materials include mechanical properties (e.g., hardness, elasticity, and strength) that influence whether the material is used in a particular design and how it are used. The strength of a material is determined by its ability to withstand an applied force or load without breaking. Structures have two forces that act within the structure – the compression force (pushing force) and the tension force (pulling force). These forces are the pushes and pulls within a structure or device that together help to support a load without breaking. Some materials can withstand high compression and high tensile forces (e.g., steel in bridges and buildings can carry a heavy load and can flex during earthquakes). Other materials can carry a heavy load but cannot withstand high tensile forces (e.g., a brick wall can carry a heavy load but will not flex during an earthquake).

The choice of materials depends on the need that is being met by the structure or device (e.g., a boat needs to be made of materials that are not susceptible to water damage; an airplane needs to be made of lightweight materials that are smooth and do not obstruct airflow). Choice of materials can affect the overall strength and stability of a structure or device.

Materials can be joined in a variety of different ways (e.g., with glue, by folding materials together, by using tape). The method use to join materials together is influenced by the type of material and the purpose of the joint (e.g., joining wood together with nails, joining art straws together with tape; making a flexible joint with a paper clip, making a rigid joint with glue). The way materials are joined can affect the overall strength and stability of the structure or device.

Tools must be matched with the appropriate material and use (e.g., saws are used to cut wood, scissors are used to cut paper). Tools should be used in a safe manner (e.g., safety glasses should be worn, drills should be in stands).

The strength and stability of a device or structure is influenced by the overall design. The strength of a structure can be enhanced in a variety of ways (e.g., layering paper together prior to folding, reinforcing art straw joints with paper triangles, bundling art straws together, incorporating bracing and triangle shapes into the structure). The stability of a structure is dependent on the overall shape and design of the structure (e.g., towers with a wide base, structures with supports buried in the ground, guy lines on tents, splayed legs on camera tripods, designs with a low center of gravity).

All technological solutions have trade-offs. Structures and devices are designed within a field of constraints (e.g., cost constraints, aesthetics constraints, material availability). Technologists must make decisions that balance these different constraints to arrive at a successful solution. Structures and devices can have positive and negative effects on the environment (e.g., the extraction of raw materials and their conversion to manufactured materials may damage the environment, responsible forest management enhances the growth of some plant species).

Website Resources

http://oecta.on.ca/curriculum/structures/grade7/7sgst3b.pdf
This website provides a series of activities on building an assortment of structures.

http://quake.wr.usgs.gov/prepare/factsheets/SaferStructures/
This website provides information about building safer structures in earthquake zones.

http://www.pbs.org/wgbh/buildingbig/bridge/index.html
This website provides ideas about bridge building, a lab on how forces affect bridges and a large variety of links to bridge building websites.

Links to the Alberta Elementary Science Program

Building Things (Grade 1); *Buoyancy and Boats* (Grade 2); *Building With a Variety of Materials* (Grade 3); *Building Devices and Vehicles that Move* (Grade 4); *Mechanisms Using Electricity* (Grade 5); *Flight* (Grade 6)

Typical Activities for Children 15: Designing and Building Technological Structures

Concept:
Properties of Materials Affects Structural Strength and Stability

Typical activities:

- Identifying strength, flexibility and buoyancy of materials that allows them to be used for difference purposes in a design. (e.g., an item of sports clothing or a container to carry groceries).

- Placing materials and objects in a sequence according to one or more attributes (e.g., sequence a set of materials by the level at which they float in water).

- Visiting a local construction site to learn more about why particular types of rocks and rock products are used in construction.

- Building models from paper, from clay, and from wood sticks and subsequently comparing the various models.

- Observing and comparing local buildings seen on a neighborhood walk.

Concept:
Materials Can be Joined in a Variety of Ways

Typical activities:

- Comparing materials that are joined in a variety of ways (e.g., comparing paper joined by different types of glue for strength and drying time, comparing art straws joined with glue versus tape versus paper clips).

Concept:
Tools Must be Matched to Appropriate Materials and Task

Typical activities:

- Using tools in a manner that ensures personal safety and the safety of others.

- Selecting and using tools to manipulate materials and build structures and devices (e.g., use various materials and tools to construct an art straw bridge).

Concept:
The Design of the Structure Affects Structural Strength and Stability

Typical activities:

- Building model boats using a variety of material and designs and testing them for the load each can carry (e.g., boats made from aluminum foil, clay, and wax paper).

- Building model furniture for a model house (e.g., chairs, tables and bedroom furniture).

Concept:
Technological Solutions Have Trade-Offs

Typical activities:

- Understanding that no technological solution is perfect. Evaluating a technological device or product for its positive and negative effects on society and the environment (e.g., satellite dishes allow people to access many television channels, provide employment for technicians, support businesses that sell satellite dishes, make for less aesthetically pleasing neighborhoods, and use a finite resource).

- Investigating technological devices and products and the constraints that shaped their development and manufacture (e.g., cost of materials, aesthetics, durability, and availability of materials).

- Evaluating a structure with respect to reliability, function, cost and appearance and suggesting improvements to a design or constructed object.

- Describing how technological products can be used to conserve natural resources.

Designing and Building Devices That Move

Devices that move require some energy source (e.g., wind can move a windmill, electricity can cause an electric vehicle to move, solar energy can cause a solar vehicle to move, muscle can move a lawnmower, and moving water can move a water wheel).

The design of a device allows energy is converted to movement (e.g., tilted vanes on a windmill, wheels on a lawnmower, and electricity powering an electric motor). The design of a device also allows energy to be transferred within the device (e.g., through pulleys, gears, and belts). Components of the design are used to control the energy and the transfer of energy within the device (e.g., switches, differentials, and gear type and size).

To stop a device from moving, some force must be applied to the device (e.g., brake) or the energy source must be withdrawn (e.g., disconnecting from an electrical source).

All technological solutions have trade-offs. Devices that move are designed within a field of constraints (e.g., cost constraints, aesthetics constraints, material availability). Technologists must make decisions that balance these different constraints to arrive at a successful solution. Structures and devices can have positive and negative effects on society and on the environment (e.g., vehicles can allow us to move at a faster rate but may add to atmospheric pollution).

Website Resources

http://www.teachingideas.co.uk/dt/contents.htm
This website provides a variety of design technology teaching ideas and activities for teachers.

http://www.shambles.net/pages/staff/DesignTec/
This website provides a long list of hotlinks to websites that feature activities for teachers and children.

Links to the Alberta Elementary Science Program

Buoyancy and Boats (Grade 2); *Building Devices and Vehicles That Move* (Grade 4); *Mechanisms Using Electricity* (Grade 5); *Flight* (Grade 6)

Typical Activities for Children 16: Designing and Building Devices That Move

Concept:
Movement Requires an Energy Source

Typical activities:

- Designing and building solar powered vehicles.

- Investigating the motion of a variety of devices (e.g., rubber balls, venetian blinds, spring-operated toys, and battery operated toys).

Concept:
The Design of a Device Allows Energy to be Converted to Movement

Typical activities:

- Demonstrating the use of rollers, wheels and axles in moving objects.

- Defining components of a design and identifying their role in the design (e.g., the fuselage on an aircraft, a rudder on a boat, the axles of a vehicle).

- Investigate different designs that fly or glide through the air in a controlled direction or a predetermined pattern of flight (e.g., paper airplanes that are able to fly loops or paper airplanes that are able to fly long, straight distances).

- Inventing a device that moves and developing a way to control or change its movement (e.g., a way to get an electricity powered vehicle to turn in different directions).

Concept:
Movement Can Be Stopped

Typical activities:

- Investigating how vehicles can be stopped (e.g., gravity powered vehicles, electricity powered vehicles).

Concept:
All Technological Solutions Have Trade-Offs

- Understanding that no technological solution is perfect. Evaluating a technological device or product for its positive and negative effects on society and the environment (e.g., gas lawnmowers allow people to keep an aesthetically pleasing lawn, provide employment for landscapers, support businesses that sell gas and make lawnmowers, pollute the atmosphere, and use a finite resource).

- Investigating technological devices and products and the constraints that shaped their development and manufacture (e.g., cost of materials, aesthetics, durability, and availability of materials).

Nature of and Relationship Between Science and Technology

Studying the nature of and relationship between science and technology allows students to explore some of the ideas presented in textbook chapters 1 and 3. By studying the nature of and relationship between science and technology students can learn how they are creative, human activities that develop in a social context. Studying the history of scientific and technological ideas helps students to understand that ideas are subject to change, with some ideas more likely to change than others.

In K–7 classrooms, students usually study:

- **Relationships between science and technology** (e.g., science and technology are interdependent and embedded in the societal context).

- **Science and technology as human endeavors** (e.g., science and technology require certain human abilities).

- **Nature of science and technology** (e.g., scientific and technological knowledge are incomplete and subject to change).

- **Nature of technology** (e.g., technological innovations can sometimes lead to new scientific knowledge).

Science in Context 5: History and Nature of Science in Maps of the Earth and Sky shows how concepts in the history and nature of science have influenced a familiar context–maps of the earth and sky. Studying this area will help students think about the human stories behind familiar events and experiences.

Part C

Science in Context 5

History and Nature of Science in Maps of the Earth and Sky

Map reading is a context that can be used to understand how concepts associated with the history and nature of science can be used to explain activities from everyday life. For instance, when you look at a map of the world you see the locations and names of bodies of land and water and areas of population. The map has lines of latitude and longitude used to help describe location, and information such as elevation above or below sea level describes mountains, valleys, and oceans.

In our lifetimes changes have been made to the names of countries, as well as to their borders, but it is easy to think that the continents have always been where they are now. In 1915, however, Alfred Wegener suggested that the continents were really plates that could move around the earth's surface and that two hundred million years ago, the continents were all grouped in close proximity. He based his hypothesis on studies he conducted on the similarities among fossil records and glacial deposits found on different continents. All but a small group of scientists dismissed his work because it challenged many then-current beliefs about geology and undermined the scientific consensus. Years later, technology caught up to Wegener's ideas and provided an instrument capable of measuring changing magnetic fields on the surface of the ocean floor. These measurements showed that Wegener had been right; now his ideas about continental drift are presented in scientific textbooks as fact. This story about Wegener shows that much always remains to be understood and that sometimes it is difficult to gain acceptance for new ideas. Disproving current ideas calls for careful research, open communication with others in the field, and often, as in the case of Wegener, technology that can lend precision and credence to new claims.

Maps of the world also reflect the historical period when they were created. In 150 AD, Ptolemy drew a map of the known world that included only Europe, a part of the Middle East, and the northern half of Africa. In 1271, Marco Polo extended current maps to include information about his journeys through the Middle East and Asia. In the 1400s, Portuguese traders searching for a spice route to the East sailed further than existing maps. They rounded the southern tip of Africa and changed the look of all subsequent maps.

Maps of the sky tell stories about the history and nature of science. Early star observations, made with the human eye alone, by astronomers in Arabia, Greece, China, southeast Asia, and other areas of the world have all contributed to our present understanding. The ancient Greeks (the Cycladic civilization—3200 BC to 1100 BC) steered their ships by landmarks and the stars. Malaysians and Indonesians (2000 BC to 1000 AD) settled the islands of Polynesia by using information about winds, sea currents, and the stars to navigate unknown waters. They made star maps of palm sticks and shells to aid in navigation. Chinese astronomers (1300 BC to 300 BC) recorded eclipses of the sun and moon, and the movement of comets. They made star charts and related the changing seasons to the apparent movement of the stars. Chinese astronomers (between 850 AD and 1059 AD) also invented the magnetic compass, which aided navigation and the drawing of land maps. Arab astronomers helped perfect the Greek astrolabe, which allowed early navigators to measure the positions of stars and planets and plot how far north or south they had traveled.

Observing the night sky, plotting star maps, and wondering about the patterns of apparent movement all helped astronomers formulate ideas about our solar system and the universe. In 150 AD, Ptolemy synthesized current ideas about astronomy and presented a view of the universe in which the earth was a fixed, unmoving mass at the center of the universe (geocentricity). This model of the universe proved useful for predicting the changing positions of stars and planets. Discrepancies were accounted for by adjusting the model. With time, however, Ptolemy's model began to prove cumbersome, and astronomers claimed it failed to account for their observations and theories. In 1514, Copernicus (1473–1543), who studied mathematics, astronomy, and other fields, set out a model of a universe with the sun at its center (heliocentricity). This view of the universe met with skepticism and generated controversy, because it was interpreted as challenging current philosophical and religious beliefs. Humankind was no longer at the center of the universe, and, perhaps, neither was the dogma of the dominant religion. Galileo and Bruno, who agreed with Copernicus, suffered serious consequences. Bruno was burned at the stake, and Galileo was imprisoned and forced to renounce his beliefs. Another 150 years passed before Newton's theory of universal gravitation provided theoretical support for Copernicus's view of the universe and movement within it and changed forever our view of our place in the universe.

Maps of the earth and sky, therefore, represent much more than information about landforms, water, and celestial movement. Instead, they tell the latest installment of a story that stretches back to earlier time–a story that still stands to change as scientists formulate and test explanations for how they see the world.

Relationships Between Science and Technology

Science and technology are interdependent and embedded in the societal context (e.g., science influences technology and technology influences science; both science and technology are influenced by social factors and, in turn, influence society). Science and technology are reciprocal. Science helps drive technology (e.g., sophisticated questions sometimes demand better instruments). Technology is essential to science (e.g., technology provides instruments, tools, and techniques). Instruments and tools help scientists to make better observations and measurements (e.g., telescopes, rulers, microscopes, and barometers).

Technology influences society through its associated products and processes (e.g., vehicles, computers, and clothing). Social needs, attitudes, and values influence the direction of technological innovation (e.g., we value fitness, and therefore we have fitness machines).

Science and technology change over time (e.g., ideas about the earth's place in the universe; typewriters giving way to computers). Human innovation can have varying benefits and drawbacks (e.g., vaccines, pesticides, and herbicides).

Website Resources

http://www.canteach.ca/links/linkaviation.html
This website features links to websites about aviation, aviation history, and the relationship between scientific ideas and aviation technology.

http://www.ncsu.edu.chass/mds/stslinks.html
This website features links to STS-related information sources.

http://echo.gmu.edu/center.php
This website provides links to science and technology in different historical periods.

http://www.si.edu/history_and_culture/history_of_science_and_technology/

This Smithsonian website provides information about historical representations of science, the history of astronomy, the history of industry, machines and electricity, and other historical examples of science and technology.

Links to the Alberta Elementary Science Program

Ideas about the relationships between science and technology should be integrated into all units within the program.

Typical Activities for Children 17: Relationships Between Science and Technology

Concept:
Science and Technology Are Interrelated and Reciprocal

Typical activities:

- Investigating how science and technology are interdependent and embedded in the social context. Selecting a technological device, explaining the science behind the device, and relating the device to what is valued in our society.

- Investigating how technology influences science and science influences technology.

- Investigating historical examples of technological devices that were made and used prior to understanding the science behind the device.

- Investigating the values that gave rise to common technological devices and products (e.g., social values that lead people to purchase SUVs, computers, microwave ovens, furniture, rugs, tanning beds, and high-end sneakers).

- Investigating how science and technology have changed over time. Identifying a common product or device or idea and tracing its history back to early times (e.g., tracing the history of ideas about the earth's place in the universe, stoves, bathroom fixtures, kitchenware, waterproof clothing, or eating utensils).

- Describing how science and technology have changed the way people work, live, and interact with their environment (e.g., comparing transportation methods over the last century and how they affected people's lives).

- Investigating how human innovation has both benefits and drawbacks. Selecting a product and compiling a list of associated benefits and drawbacks (e.g., vehicles have allowed large numbers of people to move quickly but they have also added to air pollution).

- Science can help the development of technological products (e.g., understanding electromagnetism helped in the development of microwave ovens).

- Technology can help the development of scientific ideas (e.g., telescopes helped develop our understanding of things far away; microscopes helped develop our understanding of things too small to see with the naked eye).

Nature of Science and Technology

Scientific and technological knowledge will never be complete. Scientists and technologists have learned much through inquiry and problem-solving, but much more remains to be understood (e.g., whether life can exist elsewhere than on earth).

Scientific and technological ideas can change. Scientific ideas are tentative and subject to change, with some ideas more likely to change than others (e.g., a scientific hypothesis is more likely to change than a scientific law—the hypothesis that there is water on Mars is more likely to change than the law of gravity). Technological ideas change as new ideas and innovations give way to old (e.g., typewriters giving way to computers).

Scientific inquiry involves formulating, testing and evaluating explanations. Scientists formulate and test explanations of natural phenomena using observation, experiments, and theoretical and mathematical models. Scientists may disagree with each other in the process of working towards consensus (e.g., about the origins of the earth and about the reasons why dinosaurs became extinct). Scientists question each other's findings through open communication and responding to criticism (e.g., in scientific journals and at conferences).

Technological problem-solving involves identifying some human want or need, formulating specifications for the technological solution, generating alternative ideas and proposals, selecting and implementing a final solution, and evaluating that solution. Technologists (e.g., engineers, industrial designers) use language and visual representations to negotiate constraints (e.g., cost, availability of materials, weather, friction and aesthetics) and arrive at some consensus (e.g., about how to connect wheels to an axles). Perfect technological solutions do not exist.

Website Resources

HISTORY OF TECHNOLOGY
http://www.refstar.com/techhist
This website contains an annotated collection of website links devoted to the history of technology.

SCIENCE AS A HUMAN ENDEAVOR AND THE HISTORY OF SCIENCE
http://sln.fi.edu/franklin/rotten.html
This website contains the story of the biography of Ben Franklin and his inventions.

http://www.canteach.ca/links/linkscibios.html
This website features links to people in science resources including African American scientists, female scientists, and scientists from an assortment of countries.

http://www.gap.dcs.st~and.ac.uk/~history/Mathematicians/Copernicus/html
This website features information on the life and ideas of Copernicus.

THE NATURE OF SCIENCE
http://www.enchantedlearning.com/subjects/astronomy/planets/earth
This website provides information about the Greenhouse Effect and links to other websites that feature this topic.

Links to the Alberta Elementary Science Program

Ideas about the nature of science and technology should be integrated into all units within the program.

Typical Activities for Children 18: Nature of Science and Technology

Concept:
Scientific and Technological Knowledge Will Never Be Complete

Typical activities:

- Investigating scientific and technological questions that remain controversial or unanswered (e.g., What happened to the dinosaurs? Why do we age? How did the world begin? Will we ever achieve cold fusion? Is there a cure for cancer? What energy sources will replace fossil fuels? Should we spray against mosquitoes in the city?).

Concept:
Scientific and Technological Ideas Can Change

Typical activities:

- Investigating the differences between scientific laws, theories, hypotheses, and principles. Understanding that some scientific ideas are less likely to change than others.

- Describing examples of devices and innovations that have supplanted what was considered to be commonly used technology (e.g., long play record albums, eight tracks, cassettes, compact discs).

Concept:
Scientific Inquiry Involves Formulating, Testing, and Evaluating Explanations

Typical activities:

- Exploring the nature of scientific inquiry by having the children analyze their own work in the classroom. Understanding that scientific inquiry involves formulating and testing ideas.

- Investigating how scientists work through controversies and try to reach consensus (e.g., by evaluating and challenging each other's work and pointing out statements that go beyond the evidence).

- Investigating similarities and differences between scientific inquiry and technological design (e.g., scientific inquiry is focused on the natural world, technological design is focused on the manufactured world, and both reflect what society values).

- Analyzing classroom activities to identify the differences and similarities between scientific and technological activities (e.g., abilities used to study the melting rate of ice cubes may be somewhat different from abilities used to design and make a model bridge out of wooden sticks).

Concept:
Technological Problem-Solving Involves Designing a Solution to Some Need

Typical activities:

- Selecting and using tools in manipulating materials and in building models (e.g., select appropriate materials to build a model gravity powered vehicle).

- Identifying needs met by common technological devices (e.g., needs met by refrigerators, bicycles, bridges, furniture and toys).

- Designing a plan that leads to building a model that meets some need (e.g., designing and building a paper straw tower).

Concept:
Technological Solutions Have Trade-Offs

Typical activities:

- Understanding that no technological solution is perfect. Evaluating a technological device or product for its positive and negative effects on society and the environment (e.g., gas lawnmowers allow people to keep an aesthetically pleasing lawn, provide employment for landscapers, support businesses that sell gas and make lawnmowers, pollute the atmosphere, and use a finite resource).

- Investigating technological devices and products and the constraints that shaped their development and manufacture (e.g., cost of materials, aesthetics, durability, and availability of materials).

Social and Environmental Contexts of Science and Technology

Studying social and environmental contexts of science and technology provides students with a means to understand and make decisions about environmental (e.g., how we use finite natural resources) and **social** (e.g., overpopulation) issues. Teachers should emphasize connections among science, technology, and society and encourage students to develop decision-making skills, exercise critical judgment, consider a number of perspectives, and move from applying ideas in local contexts to applying ideas in global contexts. Studying the history of science and technology helps understand how cultural and intellectual contexts have influenced science and technology which have in turn influenced the world.

In K–7 programs, students usually study:

- Interactions between human populations and the earth's resources (e.g., burning the limited supply of fossil fuels).

- Natural and human-influenced environmental changes (e.g., droughts versus urban growth).

- Ways in which science and technology have changed the ways people live, work and interact with the environment (e.g., how people have heated or lighted their homes over time).

- Contributions of diverse people to science and technology (e.g., Canadians who have contributed to science and technology).

Science in Context 6: Social and Environmental Contexts of Science and Technology in City Living shows how environmental and social perspectives are involved in a familiar context–city living. Studying this area will help students consider the STS decision making behind many of our everyday actions.

Part C

Science in Context 6

Social and Environmental Contexts of Science and Technology in City Living

City living is a context that can be used to understand how the concepts of science in personal and social perspectives influence many aspects of our everyday lives. For instance, when you awaken to the sound of your radio you are greeted with the day's air quality index. This measurement of air pollutants is constantly monitored because it indicates whether residents with respiratory illnesses can safely engage in active outdoor pursuits. The index is influenced by pollutants derived from the burning of fossil fuels, particles blown into the city by winds, a lack of air circulation, and in the winter time, temperature inversions.

As you leave your apartment and survey the crowded streets, you remember your grandparents' comments about life in the twenty-first century. "Why is everyone in such a hurry?" is one of their favorite questions. "Why do people think they need computers, bank machines, and video games?" and "Why do people always need new stuff?" You ask yourself, "Why indeed?" "How did our lives and our values change so much?"

As you walk down the street on your way to the gym, you notice a construction site for yet another high-rise apartment building. Once again, the population density of the neighborhood will be climbing, and you wonder about the potential effects on traffic conditions, crime, and local businesses. Along the street you see piles of bagged garbage that have been left on the sidewalk for pickup, and you wonder how long it will take before local landfills are at capacity. As you pass a small park, you remember that the park used to be much larger. Urban growth encroached on the parkland before city politicians put a halt to this practice and made the park a protected area. Outside buildings, you see small groups of smokers lighting up. These people have made the personal decision to smoke, and voters have made the social decision to exclude secondhand smoke from public buildings. As you approach a street corner, you wait for a break in the traffic and then dash across the street against the light. You have made the decision that this is one traffic rule you are willing to disobey, as you believe that checking oncoming traffic and then proceeding is a low-risk behavior.

When you arrive at the gym you change clothes and then begin some treadmill work. Surrounding you are people working on their cardiovascular fitness and toning their muscles. The exercise machines and weights are examples of technology that reflect how we value fitness. The technology was designed and constructed using scientific concepts associated with simple machines, properties of materials, and life science. You gaze up at the ceiling and feel glad that the asbestos has now been removed from the interior of the building. Scientists from many countries showed that asbestos could affect people's respiratory health; subsequently, laws were passed mandating its removal from existing structures.

On the way home you buy a bottle of water and reflect on your decision to avoid drinking tap water. Although you realize that tap water is constantly monitored for harmful substances, you still think you should drink bottled water–a personal decision that has been challenged by scientific research. As you toss your empty bottle into a recycling bin, you think about all the resources you require to meet your needs and to maintain your lifestyle. As you reenter your apartment building, you consider the small place you fill in the life of the city and muse, "Can one person really make a difference?"

Using Resources Responsibly

Resources are required to meet the needs and wants of populations. Some resources are derived from earth's resources (e.g., food, fuel, and building materials). Some resources are nonmaterial (e.g., serenity and security). Resource supply is finite (e.g., amount of fossil fuels). Practicing the 3 Rs (recycle, reuse, and reduce) can help extend finite resources.

Website Resources

USING RESOURCES RESPONSIBLY

http://www.canteach.ca/links/linkgenenergy.html
This website contains links to websites about energy use, alternative energy sources, and renewable energy.

IMPACT OF RESOURCE USE
http://www.esd.ornl.gov/programs/ecorisk/ecorisk.html
This website contains background information on various ecological risks such as air pollutants, petroleum contaminated sites, and wastewater treatment risks.

Links to the Alberta Elementary Science Program

Waste and Our World (Grade 4)

Typical Activities for Children 19: Using Resources Responsibly

Concept:

Resources Are Required to Meet the Needs and Wants of Populations

Typical activities:

- Investigating the differences between material and nonmaterial resources (e.g., air, water, and soil are material resources, whereas security and quiet places are nonmaterial resources).

- Investigating how resources are finite (e.g., fossil fuels and fresh water).

- Exploring and practicing ways to extend finite resources (e.g., recycling, reusing, and reducing usage). Monitoring paper used in the classroom and devising an action plan for reducing paper usage.

- Investigating how motor oil, tires, pop cans, plastic containers, and paper products can be recycled. Analyzing whether we need so many products.

- Investigating how plastic containers and grocery bags can be reused in the home.

- Examining electrical bills and identifying patterns related to peak use periods.

- Carrying out a household inventory of electrical appliances and light bulbs noting bulb wattage and describing patterns.

- Comparing past and current needs, and describing ways in which science and technology have changed lives (e.g., compare transportation methods used in the 21st century to cover large distances).

- Classifying wastes that are biodegradable and those that are not. Exploring waste disposal within the local community.

- Monitoring lunch waste in the classroom and devising an action plan for reducing non-biodegradable waste.

- Investigating how composting can reduce the need for synthetic fertilizers and topsoil.

Causing Changes to Environments

Environments are subject to change. Environments are the space, conditions, and other factors that affect the survival of individuals and populations (e.g., water availability and air quality). Environmental changes can occur naturally or be influenced by humans (e.g., through erosion, earthquakes, landslides, overpopulation, pollution, urban growth, and waste disposal). Environmental changes can occur rapidly or slowly (e.g., droughts can cause rapid changes, whereas weathering causes slow changes). Environmental degradation varies among regions and countries. Maintaining environmental health requires constant monitoring of conditions (e.g., monitoring soil, water, and air).

Website Resources

NATURAL CHANGES TO ENVIRONMENTS
http://www.canteach.callinks/linkdisaster.html
This website contains links to other websites about earthquakes, volcanoes, hurricanes, floods, and other natural disasters.

HUMAN CAUSED CHANGES TO ENVIRONMENTS
http://www.esd.ornl.gov/programs/ecorisk/ecorisk.html
This website contains background information on various ecological risks such as air pollutants, petroleum contaminated sites, and wastewater treatment risks.

Links to the Alberta Elementary Science Program

Needs of Plants and Animals (Grade 1); *Animal Life Cycles* (Grade 3); *Waste and Our World* (Grade 4); *Plant Growth and Changes* (Grade 4); *Weather Watch* (Grade 5); *Wetland Ecosystems* (Grade 5); *Trees and Forests* (Grade 6)

Typical Activities for Children 20: Causing Changes to Environments

Concept:

Environments Are Subject to Change

Typical activities:

- Understanding that environments include a variety of factors that favor survival for some living thing (e.g., water, warmth, air, and space to grow).

- Investigating and classifying environmental changes as natural or human influenced (e.g., earthquakes are a natural environmental change, whereas pollution is mostly caused by humans).

- Investigating intended and unintended effects of scientific or technological change (e.g., the effects of using lake water in the production of coal-derived electricity).

- Describing the potential impact of the use by humans on natural resources (e.g., devise a plan for reducing the amount of lunch refuse discarded by the school).

- Investigating ways in which to monitor environmental health (e.g., water quality studies and monitoring air pollutants).

Diverse People Contribute to Science and Technology

Science and technology are human endeavors. Science and technology have been practiced throughout human history (e.g., early Arab astronomy, and early Chinese chemistry).

Diverse groups of people work in science and technology (e.g., women and men, and people from different countries. Science and technology benefit from the variety of people engaged in these pursuits (e.g., women and men, and people from different countries).

Scientists and technologists work in a variety of settings (e.g., at universities and in industry). Scientists and technologists operate under ethical codes (e.g., codes regulating how human subjects can be involved in research projects). Scientists and technologists do not have all the answers for the world's problems (e.g., how to resolve national and ethnic conflicts; how to make completely risk free products).

Website Resources

DIVERSITY OF SCIENTISTS AND TECHNOLOGISTS
http://sln.fi.edu/franklin/rotten.html
This website contains the story of the biography of Ben Franklin and his inventions.

http://www.canteach.ca/links/linkscibios.html
This website features links to people in science resources including African American scientists, female scientists, and scientists from an assortment of countries.

http://inventors.about.com
This website contains information about the diverse people who have invented various technological inventions.

Links to the Alberta Elementary Science Program

Ideas about the diversity of people who have contributed to science and technology should be integrated into all units within the program.

Typical Activities for Children 21: Diverse People Contribute to Science and Technology

Concept:
Science and Technology Are Human Endeavors

Typical activities:

- Investigating historical examples of science and technology (e.g., early machines, Arab astronomy, Greek architecture, Egyptian engineering, Aztec astronomy, and Chinese chemistry).

- Investigating historical examples of how scientific theories can be met with opposition or acceptance (e.g., believing that the sun circles the earth versus believing that the earth circles the sun; believing that the earth is flat versus believing that the earth is a sphere).

Concept:
Science and Technology Advance Through the Contributions of Various People and Cultures

Typical activities:

- Finding out about a variety of people who have had successful careers in science and technology. Selecting a person and writing a report on his or her career.

- Identifying people in the local community who work in science- or technology-related careers (e.g., a meteorologist, a wildlife biologist, an environmental chemist, a water treatment technician, a restaurant inspector, a nurse, a lab technician, and a physiotherapist); investigating what they do in their jobs and the kinds of science and technology training they have.

- Researching examples of Canadians who have contributed to science and technology.

- Describing scientific and technological activities carried out by people from different cultures.

- Investigating the kinds of workplaces in which science and technology careers are pursued (e.g., industries, small businesses, and universities).

- Investigating the ethical codes under which scientists and technologists work (e.g., professional codes of conduct and codes regulating how human participants can be involved in research projects).

- Investigating the limits of scientific and technological knowledge. Identifying an ongoing environmental or technological problem and the efforts that have been made to solve it (e.g., how scientists and technologists have tried to solve problems of famines, floods, diseases, air pollution, hearing impairment, global warming, and land reclamation).

Part D
Concepts Related to the Alberta Elementary Science Program Topics

Note:
In the following sections, General Concepts are in bold and Specific Concepts are in regular type.

Concepts Related to the Alberta Elementary Science Program Topics

Part D

Grade 1

Topic 1A: Creating Colour

Concepts Underlying Specific Learning Expectations

1. **The primary colors of pigment (paint) are red, yellow and blue (SLE 4).**

    1.1 Combinations of primary colors make secondary colors (e.g., orange, purple) (SLE 4).

    1.2 A color that matches a given sample can be created by mixing the appropriate amounts of primary colors (SLE 5).

2. **Colors and paints can be classified according to their properties (SLE 2, SLE 6 and SLE 8).**

    2.1 Paints can be classified according to their optical properties (e.g., transparency, translucency, and opacity) (SLE 6)

    2.1.1 The optical properties of paint can be manipulated (e.g., by adding white to the paint or making a very thin layer of the paint) (SLE 2 and 7).

    2.2 Paints can be classified according to their ability to adhere to different surfaces (e.g., paper, fabrics, and plastics) (SLE 8).

3. **Colors can be found in natural objects (e.g., rocks, trees and animals) and manufactured objects (e.g., clothing, automobiles, and kitchenware) (SLE 1).**

    3.1 Dyes can be extracted from plants (e.g., yellow from goldenrod and green from ragweed) (SLE 9).

    3.1.1 Dyes can be applied to a cloth by dissolving and transferring to a water-soluble paint (SLE 9).

4. **White light can be separated into colors (e.g., in rainbows, with light filters and by prisms) (SLE 10).**

Special Note About SLE 10: In this unit, addressing questions related to seeing colors of light directly (rather than colors reflected by pigments) may be confusing. Colors of light are different from and behave differently than colored pigments. For example, the primary colors of light are red, blue, and green. Colors of pigments are subtractive while colors of light are additive. You should research this thoroughly before teaching about it.

Topic 1B: Seasonal Changes

Concepts Underlying Specific Learner Expectations

1. **Some events occur at regular intervals of time (e.g., day length changes with the seasons) (SLE 1, 2).**

    1.1 Weather changes occur from day to day and across the seasons (e.g., rain and snow) (SLE 1).

    1.2 Seasonal changes occur in a yearly cycle (e.g., spring and winter) (SLE 1, 4).

    1.2.1 Plants change on a seasonal basis (e.g., changes in appearance) (SLE 2).

    1.2.2 Animals change on a seasonal basis (e.g., change in activity) (SLE 2).

    1.2.2.1 Humans make preparations for seasonal change (e.g., change in clothing) (SLE 3).

Topic 1C: Building Things

Concepts Underlying Specific Learner Expectations

1. **Structures and devices can be made with a variety of materials (e.g., plastic, paper, and wood) (SLE 1).**

    1.1 The choice of materials depends on the need being met by the structure or device (e.g., strong materials for load bearing structures). (SLE 1).

    1.2 Materials can be joined in a variety of different ways (e.g., with glue) (SLE 1).

    1.3 Materials can be strengthened in a variety of ways (e.g., folding, layering, and combining with other materials) (SLE 1).

2. **Structures and devices are designed to meet some need (SLE 4).**

    2.1 Structures and devices are constructed of purposeful components (e.g., model homes have a variety of rooms that fulfill different purposes) (SLE 2).

3. **Two structures or devices can have corresponding parts (e.g., comparing the parts of a pen to that of a pencil) (SLE 3).**

Topic 1D: Senses

Concepts Underlying Specific Learner Expectations

1. **The senses are used to help gather information to interpret the world (SLE 1, 3).**

    1.1 Eyes are used to gather visual information (e.g., colors and depth perception) (SLE 1,3).

    1.2 Ears are used to gather auditory information (e.g., high pitch and low sounds) (SLE 1,3).

    1.3 A nose gathers olfactory information (e.g., sharp smells and floral smells) (SLE 1,3).

    1.4 A mouth gathers gustatory information (e.g., sweet, sour, and salty tastes) (SLE 1,3).

    1.5 Touch gathers tactile information (e.g., shape and texture) (SLE 1,3).

2. **Living things have different abilities to sense the world (e.g., some animals have a better sense of smell than other animals) (SLE 5).**

    2.1 Human senses have limitations (e.g., eyes cannot detect all movement and a head cold can distort taste and smell) (SLE 4).

    2.1.1 Humans can adapt to some sensory limitations (e.g., optical lenses for near-sightedness and hearing aids for partial deafness) (SLE 6).

3. **Senses contribute to the safety and quality of life (e.g., can help anticipate danger, help to locate food and recognize own young) (SLE 2).**

4. **Sensory organs need care (e.g., avoiding very loud noises and avoiding looking into bright light sources) (SLE 7).**

Topic 1E: Needs of Animals and Plants

Concepts Underlying Specific Learner Expectations

1. **Living things exhibit a variety of characteristics that distinguish them from nonliving things (e.g., they grow, require food or manufacture their own food) (SLE 1, 2, 6).**

    1.1 Animals have requirements to maintain life (e.g., food and water) (SLE 6).

    1.2 Plants have requirements to maintain life (e.g., light and growing media) (SLE 7, 8).

2. **Population size reflects the interdependency of plants and animals (e.g., as shown by food chains) (SLE 2, 10).**

    2.1 Animals depend on plants (e.g., for food and shelter) (SLE 10). Plants benefit from animals (e.g., from seed dispersal) (SLE 10).

3. **Plants and animals adapt to their environments (e.g., thick fur in cold environments and ways to store moisture in dry environments) (SLE 9).**

4. **Some plants and animals are wild others are domesticated (SLE 5).**

5. **Living things can be grouped according to common characteristics (SLE 4).**

    5.1 Animals can be grouped according to common characteristics (e.g., mammals or birds) (SLE 4).

    5.2 Plants can be grouped according to common characteristics (e.g., conifers and deciduous trees) (SLE 4).

Grade 2

Topic 2A: Exploring Liquids

**Concepts Underlying Specific
Learner Expectations**

1. **Matter and materials can be changed
(SLE 1, 5, 6, 7).**

   1.1 Most matter exists as a solid, liquid or gas (SLE 1).

   1.2 Matter can change in state with the addition or removal of energy (e.g., water can exist as a solid [ice], as a liquid and as a gas [vapor]) (SLE 5, 6).

2. **Matter has distinctive properties (SLE 1, 2).**

   2.1 Properties allow matter to be distinguished from one another (e.g., color, interactions with other matter, absorbency, density, viscosity) (SLE 2, 3).

3. **Structures and devices can be made with a variety of materials (SLE 4).**

   3.1 Choice of materials depends on the need being met by the structure or device (SLE 4).

4. **Water is a unique substance (SLE 8).**

   4.1 Water is needed by all living things (SLE 8).

5. **Maintaining environmental health requires constant monitoring of conditions (e.g., water) (SLE 9).**

Topic 2B: Buoyancy and Boats

**Concepts Underlying Specific
Learner Expectations**

1. **Structures and devices can be made with a variety of materials (e.g., plastic, paper and wood) (SLE 1).**

   1.1 The choice of materials depends on the need being met by the structure or device (e.g., waterproof materials for boats). (SLE 1, 6).

   1.2 Materials can be joined in a variety of different ways (e.g., with glue) (SLE 3).

   1.3 Materials can be manipulated in a variety of ways (e.g., waxing paper increases its ability to be waterproof) (SLE 6).

1.4 Materials can be classified according to a variety of properties (e.g., classifying materials on the basis of buoyancy) (SLE 1).

1.5 Materials can be evaluated (SLE 6).

2. **Structures and devices are designed to meet some need (SLE 4, 7, 8).**

   2.1 Structures and devices are constructed of purposeful components (e.g., model boats have a variety of parts that fulfill different purposes) (SLE 2, 3, 4, 5).

   2.2 Designs can be modified to fit changing needs (SLE 2, 3, 4, 5).

   2.2 Designs can be evaluated (e.g., buoyancy of the boat and load it can carry without sinking) (SLE 9).

3. **Tools must be matched with the appropriate material and use (e.g., saws are used to cut wood, scissors are used to cut paper) (SLE 2, 4, 5, 7).**

   3.1 Tools should be used in a safe manner (e.g., safety glasses should be worn) (SLE 2, 4, 5, 7).

4. **Buoyancy depends on the material used and its shape (SLE 1, 2).**

Topic 2C: Magnetism

**Concepts Underlying Specific
Learner Expectations**

1. **Magnetism is a form of energy (SLE 3).**

   1.1 Magnets have polarity (e.g.. north and south poles) (SLE 4).

2. **Materials have different magnetic properties (SLE 3, 6).**

   2.1 Some materials are magnetic and some are not (e.g., iron, nickel, cobalt are attracted to magnets; copper and lead are not) (SLE 2, 3, 6).

   2.2 Magnetic materials have different magnetic strengths (SLE 7).

3. **Science and technology are interrelated and reciprocal and embedded in the societal context (SLE 1).**

   3.1 Magnetic energy can be generated from or changed to other forms of energy (e.g. power stations use magnetic energy to generated electricity; electromagnets use electricity to generate magnetic energy) (SLE 1).

Topic 2D: Hot and Cold Temperature

Concepts Underlying Specific Learner Expectations

1. **The sun is the earth's primary source of energy (heat and light) (SLE 7).**

    1.1 Heat energy can be changed into other forms of energy) (e.g., light) (SLE 7).

    1.2 Temperature is a measure of heat energy and is measured in degrees (e.g., degrees Celsius) (SLE 2).

2. **Heat can be transferred between objects and materials (SLE 3, 7, 8, 9).**

    2.1 Heat may be transferred to or from or through different materials, at different rates, from hot to cold (e.g., by conduction, convection and radiation) (SLE 8, 3).

    2.2 Heat transfer between materials can be slowed (e.g., by insulation, by having feathers) (SLE 8, 9).

    2.3 Heat flows from warmer objects to cooler ones, until both reach the same temperature (SLE 8).

    2.4 Adding heat can change the state of materials (e.g., heating water to make it boil changes its state from liquid to gas) (SLE 3).

    2.5 Removing heat can change the state of materials (e.g., cooling water can change its states from liquid to solid) (SLE 3).

3. **The choice of materials depends on the need that is being met by the structure or device (SLE 7, 10).**

4. **Resources are required to meet the needs and wants of populations (SLE 7).**

    4.1 Some resources are derived from earth's resources (e.g., fuel and building materials) (SLE 7).

    4.2 Resource supply is finite (e.g., amount of fossil fuels) (SLE 7).

Topic 2E: Small Crawling and Flying Animals

Concepts Underlying Specific Learner Expectations

1. **Biological classification takes into account the diversity of life on Earth (SLE 1, 2).**

    1.1 Animals can be grouped according to common characteristics (e.g., vertebrates and invertebrates; mammals, birds, reptiles, amphibians and fishes) (SLE 1, 2).

2. **Living things have basic needs making them distinct from nonliving things (SLE 3, 7).**

    2.1 Living things live in environments here their needs are met (SLE 3, 7).

3. **Living things have features that enable them to meet their needs (e.g., eyes collect visual information) (SLE 6).**

    3.1 Animals have features that enable them to meet their needs in special places (SLE 6).

4. **Different kinds of plant and animal populations exist in various environments (SLE 3, 5, 8).**

    4.1 Living things are affected by the nonliving features of their environments (SLE 3, 5).

    4.2 Living things can affect their environments and other living things (SLE 8).

5. **Individuals of a species occur in populations (SLE 4, 5).**

    5.1 Populations can be categorized by the functions they serve in an ecosystem (e.g., producer, consumer and decomposer) (SLE 4).

Grade 3

Topic 3A: Rocks and Minerals

Concepts Underlying Specific Learner Expectations

1. **Earth's materials include rocks, soil, water and atmospheric gases (SLE 1, 2, 3, 4, 6).**

   1.1 The earth's crust is made of different kinds of rocks and minerals (e.g., igneous, metamorphic and sedimentary rocks) (SLE 2, 3).

   1.2 Different kinds of rocks are formed in different ways (e.g., by pressure, heating and cooling) (SLE 3, 4).

   1.3 Different kinds of rocks have different properties (e.g., color, texture, hardness, luster, and presence of carbonates) (SLE 1,2, 3).

   1.4 Rocks can be broken down in different ways (e.g., by wind, water, cooling and warming and living organisms) (SLE 6).

2. **Breakdown of rock contributes to soil formation (e.g., formation of sand, silt, clay and pebbles) (SLE 5, 6).**

   2.1 Different soils have different properties (e.g., color, proportions of clay, silt, sand and plant material) (SLE 5).

3. **The choice of materials depends on the need being met by the structure or device (e.g., bricks can carry a heavy load) (SLE 7).**

Topic 3B: Building with a Variety of Materials

Concepts Underlying Specific Learner Expectations

1. **Structures and devices can be made with a variety of materials (e.g., plastic, paper and wood) (SLE 1, 2, 4).**

   1.1 The choice of materials depends on the need being met by the structure or device (e.g., wood for strength). (SLE 1, 2).

   1.2 Materials can be joined in a variety of different ways (e.g., with glue) (SLE 4).

   1.3 Materials can be manipulated in a variety of ways (e.g., waxing paper increases its ability to be waterproof) (SLE 1, 2).

   1.4 Materials can be classified according to a variety of properties (e.g., classifying materials on the basis of strength) (SLE 1).

   1.5 Materials can be evaluated (SLE 2).

2. **Tools must be matched with the appropriate material and use (e.g., saws are used to cut wood, scissors are used to cut paper) (SLE 3).**

   2.1 Tools should be used in a safe manner (e.g., safety glasses should be worn) (SLE 3).

3. **Structures and devices are designed to meet some need (SLE 5).**

   3.1 Structures and devices are constructed of purposeful components (e.g., model bridges have a variety of parts that fulfill different purposes) (SLE 5).

4. **All technological solutions have trade-offs (SLE 6).**

   4.1 Structures and devices are designed within a field of constraints (e.g., cost constraints) (SLE 6).

Topic 3C: Testing Materials and Designs

Concepts Underlying Specific Learner Expectations

1. **Building strong and stable structures is a function of the materials used, the way materials are joined together and the overall design of the structure (SLE 1,2).**

   1.1 Strength and stability can be tested (SLE 4, 5, 6).

2. **Structures and devices can be made with a variety of materials (e.g., plastic, paper and wood) (SLE 2, 3, 7).**

   1.4 The choice of materials depends on the need being met by the structure or device (e.g., strong materials for load bearing structures). (SLE 2, 3, 7).

   1.5 Materials can be joined in a variety of different ways (e.g., with glue) (SLE 2, 3, 7).

   1.6 Materials can be strengthened in a variety of ways (e.g., folding, layering and combining with other materials) (SLE 2, 3, 7).

Topic 3D: Hearing and Sound

Concepts Underlying Specific Learner Expectations

1. **Sound is a form of energy and is produced by vibrations (e.g., vibrations caused by tapping on a table or plucking a guitar string) (SLE 1, 2, 5, 10, 11).**

    1.1 The pitch of a sound depends on the rate of vibrations (e.g., rapid vibrations result in high pitch) (SLE 4).

    1.2 The intensity of a sound depends on vibration size (e.g., small vibrations result in a soft sound) (SLE 2, 3).

    1.3 Ears have nerve endings designed to detect vibrations (SLE 8).

2. **Sound vibrations travel differently through different solids, liquids and gases (e.g., Styrofoam, water and air) (SLE 7, 12).**

    2.1 Sound vibrations bounce off some surfaces (e.g., echoes in a canyon) (SLE 2).

Topic 3E: Animal Life Cycles

Concepts Underlying Specific Learner Expectations

1. **Biological classification takes into account the diversity of life on Earth (SLE 1).**

    1.1 Animals can be grouped according to common characteristics (e.g., vertebrates and invertebrates; mammals, birds, reptiles, amphibians and fishes) (SLE 1).

2. **Living things have life cycles (SLE 2, 7).**

    2.1 Animal life cycles can be classified according to similarities and differences (e.g., life cycles of insects, amphibians and reptiles are similar in some ways and different in others) (SLE 2, 7).

3. **Reproduction is a characteristic of all living systems (SLE 2, 3).**

4. **Living things have features that enable them to meet their needs (eyes collect visual information) (SLE 4, 6).**

    4.1 Animals have features that enable them to meet their needs in special places (e.g., some aquatic animals have gills and others have webbed feet) (SLE 1, 7).

5. **Offspring tend to resemble their parents (SLE 5).**

    5.1 Animal offspring generally look like their parent(s) but can differ in some ways (e.g., different sizes) (SLE 5).

6. **Extinction of species is common (SLE 8).**

    6.1 Habitat loss and adaptive capability can affect population size and existence (SLE 8).

7. **Environments are subject to change (SLE 9).**

    7.1 Environmental changes can occur naturally or be influenced by humans (e.g., through erosion, urban growth and waste disposal) (SLE 9).

Grade 4

Topic 4A: Waste and Our World

Concepts Underlying Specific Learner Expectations

1. **Plants and animals produce wastes that are recycled in nature (SLE 1).**

2. **Human activity produces waste (2, 4, 5, 7).**

   2.1 Wastes from human activity can be classified in terms of their potential harm to the environment (e.g., toxic, hazardous) (SLE 2, 4, 7).

   2.2 Consumer products are a primary source of human waste (e.g., advertising, packaging, products) (SLE 4, 5).

3. **Waste can be disposed of or used responsibly in a variety of ways (SLE 3, 6, 9, 10, 11).**

   3.1 All waste disposal methods have advantages and disadvantages (SLE 3, 6, 10).

   3.2 Wastes can be reduced (SLE 8, 12).

   3.3 Wastes can be reused or recycled (SLE 9, 11).

Topic 4B: Wheels and Levers

Concepts Underlying Specific Learner Expectations

1. **Simple machines such as levers, rollers, and wheels and axles make work easier (SLE 1, 2).**

2. **Simple machines make work easier by transferring motion (SLE 3, 4, 5).**

   2.1 Drive systems transfer motion, e.g., wheel to wheel contact, belts, chains, and gears (3, 4).

   2.2 Changes in direction, speed, and force result from different ways of linking components through drive systems (SLE 5).

3. **Levers make work easier by multiplying movement and force (SLE 6, 7, 8).**

   3.1 Levers can apply a small movement to create a large movement (SLE 6, 7)

   3.2 Levers can apply a small force to create a large force (SLE 6, 7)

   3.3 Changes in the size of a lever or position of the fulcrum will affect the forces and movements involved (SLE 6, 7)

   3.4 Many common human devices use levers (e.g., teeter totter, scissors, pliers, tongs, nutcracker, fishing reel, wheelbarrow) (SLE 8).

Topic 4C: Building Devices and Vehicles That Move

Concepts Underlying Specific Learner Expectations

1. **Technology is designed and made to fulfill a human need or want (SLE 1, 2, 3)**

   1.1 Teamwork is an important aspect of technological design (SLE 2, 6, 7)

2. **There is no perfect design; all designs require trade-offs and compromises (e.g., speed may be increased at the expense of aesthetics) (SLE 3, 5, 7)**

   2.1 All designs have strengths and weaknesses (SLE 5, 7)

   2.2 Alternative designs may be evaluated according to agreed-upon criteria (SLE, 5, 7)

3. **A mechanical device is a technology that includes moving parts (e.g., linkages, wheels and axles) which perform a useful function (SLE 1, 2, 3, 6)**

   3.1 A vehicle is a mechanical device that transports objects or people (SLE 1, 2, 3, 6)

   3.2 Control is an important element in the design and construction of a mechanical device (SLE 4).

   3.3 Mechanical devices can be propelled by simple forces (e.g., push, pull, gravity) created by energy-storing or energy–consuming components (e.g., moving water, wind, elastic bands, springs) (SLE 2, 3, 4).

Topic 4D: Light and Shadows

Concepts Underlying Specific Learner Expectations

1. **Light is a form of energy (SLE 1).**

2. **Light emanates from a variety of sources (SLE 1, 2, 3).**

    2.1 Some objects emit their own light (e.g., the sun, electric lights, flames, materials that glow) (SLE 2).

    2.2 Most objects require an external source of light to be seen (SLE 3).

    2.3 Bright lights can damage the eye (e.g., the Sun, welding sparks) (SLE 1).

3. **Light travels outward from a source in straight lines (SLE 4).**

    3.1 Light travels through a transparent material (SLE 7, 8).

    3.2 Light travels partially through a translucent material (SLE 8).

    3.3 Light is blocked by an opaque material (SLE 4, 6, 7, 8).

4. **Opaque objects cast shadows (SLE 4, 5, 6, 8).**

    4.1 Light and shadows fall along a predictable path (SLE 5, 6).

    4.2 Shadows change in size and location when a light-casting object or a shade- casting object is moved (SLE 5, 6).

5. **The path of light can be affected by mirrors, optical devices (e.g., hand lens, telescope, microscope, camera), and prisms (9, 10, 11, 12).**

    5.1 Light can be reflected; smooth surfaces (e.g., mirrors) are good reflectors (SLE 9).

    5.2 Light can be refracted or bent (e.g., by water-filled aquaria, prisms, and lenses) (SLE 10, 11, 12).

    5.3 Light can be broken into colours (e.g., by a prism) (SLE 11).

    5.4 Different colours of light can be combined to form a new colour (e.g., red and blue light combine to make magenta) (SLE 11).

Topic 4E: Plant Growth and Changes

Concepts Underlying Specific Learner Expectations

1. **Plants are important to human beings (e.g., food, shelter, medicine) and to the environment (e.g., maintain oxygen, anchor soil) (SLE 1, 3).**

2. **Plants have different parts which serve different functions (e.g., roots, stems, leaves, flowers) (SLE 2, 10).**

    2.1 Roots help anchor the plant and absorb water and dissolved minerals (SLE 2).

    2.2 Stems support the plant, conduct water and dissolved minerals through the plant, and may make or store food (SLE 2).

    2.3 Leaves make food, give off excess water, process food, and remove waste (SLE 2).

    2.4 Flowers have the special role of helping the plant reproduce (SLE 2).

3. **Variations across plant communities are related to variations in environmental conditions (e.g., amount of water, temperature) (SLE 6).**

4. **Plants have requirements for growth (SLE 4, 5, 10).**

    4.1 Plant require air, light, water, nutrients, and space (SLE 4, 10).

    4.2 Growth requirements may vary from plant to plant, and some plants may have special needs (e.g., temperature) (SLE 4, 5).

    4.3 Variations across plant communities are related to variations in environmental conditions (e.g., precipitation) (SLE 6).

5. **Plants of the same kind go through a common life cycle (SLE 7, 8, 9, 10, 11).**

    5.1 New plants are similar to parent plants (SLE 7, 10).

    5.2 New plants can propagate from a piece of an old plant (e.g., a root, cutting, runner, or bulb) (SLE 8, 10).

    5.3 Flowering plants can also propagate through seeds (SLE 8, 9, 10).

    5.4 Seeds are distributed in various ways (e.g., wind, animals) (SLE 9, 11).

Grade 5

Topic 5A: Electricity and Magnetism

Concepts Underlying Specific Learner Expectations

1. **Electricity is a form of energy that may pose a safety hazard (e.g., household current, short circuits, bare wires, overloading an electrical circuit (SLE 1).**

2. **Electricity can produce magnetism (e.g., electromagnets) and magnetism can produce electricity (e.g., generators) (SLE 2,3).**

   2.1 Magnetic fields can be detected around magnets and around wires carrying an electrical current (e.g., using iron filings or a compass) (SLE 2, 3).

3. **An electric current flows from the source of electricity, along one path to the appliance (e.g., a bulb), and along a second path back to the source (SLE 4, 5, 6).**

   3.1 A continuous path is needed for a flow of current to occur (SLE 4).

   3.2 Materials called conductors allow electricity to flow through them (SLE 5).

   3.3 Materials called insulators do not allow electricity to flow through them (SLE 5).

   3.4 Some materials (e.g., resistors) allow a partial flow of electricity (SLE 6, 7).

4. **Visual symbol systems can express important information about electricity (SLE 8, 9, 10).**

   4.1 The amount of electricity consumed in a home can be read on an electrical meter (SLE 8, 9).

   4.2 The components that make up an electrical circuit can be represented using a circuit diagram (SLE 10).

Topic 5B: Mechanisms Using Electricity

Concepts Underlying Specific Learner Expectations

1. **Electricity is a widely utilized form of energy that is used to power a variety of helpful devices (e.g., lamp, stove, telephone, fan) (SLE 1, 2, 5, 6).**

   1.1 Purposes of electrical devices include lighting, heating, communicating, and moving (SLE 1, 2, 5, 6).

   1.2 An electric motor converts electricity into mechanical motion (SLE 5).

2. **A complete circuit is required for electricity to flow (SLE 2).**

   2.1 Control devices (e.g., switch, fuse) are essential parts of an electrical circuit (SLE 3, 4).

   2.2 A series circuit has only one path for the electrical charges to move along (SLE 7, 8).

   2.3 A parallel electrical circuit has multiple paths for the electrical charges to move along (SLE 7, 8).

3. **Technological design in the context of electricity involves using appropriate materials to plan and construct an electrical device that meets given requirements (e.g., burglar alarm) (SLE 6, 9).**

Topic 5C: Classroom Chemistry

Concepts Underlying Specific Learner Expectations

1. **A mixture is a physical combination of two or more pure substances (i.e., elements or compounds) (SLE 1,2)**

   1.1 Materials in a mixture can be separated using techniques such as filtration, screening, and sedimentation (SLE 2).

2. **A solution is a homogenous mixture of two or more substances (SLE 3, 4, 5).**

   2.1 In most common solutions the solvent or dissolving material is water and the solute or dissolved material is a solid (SLE 5).

   2.2 Solutions can be separated using techniques such as evaporation, distillation, and chromatography (SLE 3, 4).

3. **A chemical reaction is a process by which one or more substances is/are transformed into one or more new substances (SLE 6, 7, 8, 9).**

   3.1 The new substances differ in properties from the original substance(s) (SLE 6, 7, 8).

   3.2 An external indicator may accompany a reaction (e.g., colour change, production of a gas, release of heat, formation of a precipitate, an odour) (SLE 6, 8, 9).

   3.3 Most chemical reactions are not reversible (e.g., fuels burning, formation of a gas) (SLE 6, 7).

Topic 5D: Weather Watch

Concepts Underlying Specific Learner Expectations

1. **Weather describes the state of the atmosphere at a particular time and place (SLE 1, 2, 4, 5).**

   1.1 Weather is influenced by many conditions in the atmosphere (e.g., heat energy, moisture, air movement, air pressure) (SLE 2, 4, 9, 10).

   1.2 Instruments can be constructed to measure weather-related phenomena (e.g., temperature, relative humidity, air pressure, wind speed, wind direction, amount of precipitation) (SLE 5, 6, 8).

   1.3 Weather can be forecasted with some degree of accuracy (SLE 7, 8, 13).

   1.4 Particular weather conditions can pose challenges for humans (SLE 13, 14)

2. **Climate refers to long term weather trends in a particular region of the world (SLE 11, 12).**

   2.1 Human actions can affect climate (e.g., greenhouse effect) (SLE 12).

Topic 5E: Wetland Ecosystems

Concepts Underlying Specific Learner Expectations

1. **An ecosystem is an interacting system of plants, animals, humans, and the surrounding physical environment (SLE 1).**

2. **A wetland is an ecosystem defined by three characteristics: covered by water some or all of the time, has hydric soil (i.e., soil lacks enough oxygen to grow certain plants such as trees), and the plant life is adapted (e.g., pond, slough, marsh, swamp, bog) (SLE 1, 2, 3).**

   2.1 Specific adaptations make certain plants and animals suited for life in a wetland (e.g., increased buoyancy, tolerance for low oxygen levels, ability to survive flooding) (SLE 4, 8).

3. **All organisms play an important role in a wetland community (e.g., as part of a food web) (SLE 5, 6, 7).**

   3.1 A food web is a complicated system of interaction among plants, animals, and energy (SLE 6, 7).

   3.2 Different organisms play different roles in a food web (i.e., producers, consumers, decomposers) (SLE 5, 6, 7).

   3.3 Food webs are made up of smaller food chains (SLE 7).

4. **Human actions can influence wetland ecosystems, both positively and negatively (SLE 9, 10, 11).**

Grade 6

Topic 6A: Air and Aerodynamics

Concepts Underlying Specific Learner Expectations

1. **Air occupies space and has weight. (SLE 1, 2).**

   1.1 Air exerts pressure (SLE 1).

   1.2 Air can be compressed (SLE 2).

2. **Air movement across a surface creates lift (Bernoulli's Principle) (SLE 3, 4, 5).**

   2.1 Flight requires sufficient lift to overcome the force of gravity (SLE 4, 5).

3. **Thrust is a force generated by some part of an object in flight (e.g., jet engine, bird wings) that pushes the object forward through the air (SLE 6,7).**

   3.1 The thrust force must be sufficient to overcome the drag force, which is the resistance to flight created by the surrounding air (SLE 6, 7).

   3.2 Streamlining reduces drag force (SLE 7).

4. **Air is made up of different gases, mainly nitrogen (about 78%) and oxygen (about 21%) (SLE 8).**

Topic 6B: Flight

Concepts Underlying Specific Learner Expectations

1. **Knowledge of aerodynamics (e.g., lift, drag, weight, thrust) can be applied to the design, building, testing, and modification of a variety of flying devices (e.g., parachute, hot air balloon, glider, model aircraft, rocket) (SLE 1, 2, 3, 4, 5, 6).**

   1.1 When working in teams, planning, communication, cooperation, and flexibility are important to the overall result (SLE 1, 3, 5, 6).

   1.2 The rise and fall of a hot air balloon can be explained using the concepts of buoyancy and density (SLE 2).

   1.3 Stability and control in flight are important considerations in the design of aircraft (SLE 4, 5).

2. **Model aircraft and rockets may be propelled by a variety of means (SLE 5, 6, 7).**

   2.1 Model aircraft may be propelled by elastic bands, an electric motor, a pulsejet or turbojet, or a glow engine (SLE 5, 6).

   2.2 Model rockets may be powered by a balloon, water (bottle rocket), carbon dioxide, or commercially purchased chemical fuels (note: safety considerations) (SLE 7).

3. **Aircraft and spacecraft are designed differently because they are used for different purposes under different conditions (e.g., a spacecraft must escape the earth's gravitational field and must carry its own oxygen supply) (SLE 7).**

Topic 6C: Sky Science

Concepts Underlying Specific Learner Expectations

1. **The Sun, the Earth, the moon, and all the other bodies that orbit the Sun make up our solar system (SLE 1, 4, 9, 10, 12).**

   1.1 Our solar system is only a tiny fraction of the known universe (SLE 12).

2. **Our Sun is a star (SLE 1, 2, 4, 5).**

   2.1 A star is a huge, hot, glowing sphere of gas that shines by its own light (SLE 1).

   2.2 Constellations are visible patterns of stars which different peoples have given different names (e.g., Orion the Hunter [Europe] is also called the Butterfly [Cree]) (SLE 2).

3. **A planet is a ball of rock or gas of considerable mass that orbits a star (SLE 1, 9, 10).**

   3.1 Our Earth is one of nine planets that orbit the Sun (SLE 1, 3, 6).

   3.2 Earth's rotation causes the cycle of day and night (SLE 6).

   3.3 The apparent movement of objects in the night sky is regular and predictable and related to Earth's rotation (SLE 3).

3.4 The other eight planets have characteristics and surface conditions that are different from Earth (e.g., Venus is hotter, Jupiter is much larger) (SLE 9, 10).

4. **A moon is a natural rocky body of varying size that orbits regularly around a larger planet (SLE 7, 8, 10).**

4.1 Earth's moon goes through regular and predictable phases (SLE 7, 8).

4.2 Six of the other planets in our solar system have moons and these moons are similar to and different from Earth's moon (SLE 9, 10).

5. **Various technologies and procedures (e.g., telescope, space probes) have been used to gather knowledge about objects in the night sky (SLE 11).**

Topic 6D: Evidence and Investigations

Concepts Underlying Specific Learner Expectations

1. **Observation and inference skills can be used to recognize and interpret the patterns created by human and animal activity (SLE 1, 2, 3, 4).**

1.1 Evidence of activity may include footprints, tire prints, fingerprints, soil samples, ink from pens, handwriting samples, and fabric samples (SLE 1, 2).

1.2 Unique characteristics of the evidence may allow inferences to be made regarding the participants and the nature of the activity (SLE 3).

1.3 The evidence may be linked to a possible source by classifying (e.g., prints, soil samples), analyzing (e.g., ink, handwriting), and comparing (e.g., fabric samples) (SLE 4).

Topic 6E: Trees and Forests

Concepts Underlying Specific Learner Expectations

1. **A tree is a perennial seed plant, usually of a certain minimum size, with a single woody stem (SLE 4, 5, 6).**

1.1 Deciduous (hardwood) trees are better adapted to warmer climates, have broad leaves, and lose all their leaves at some time during the year (e.g., aspen, birch, maple, elm) (SLE 4, 5, 6).

1.2 Coniferous (softwood) trees are better adapted to colder climates, can grow in more extreme conditions (e.g., poor soil, high altitudes), have very narrow leaves called needles, keep their needles year around, and bear their seeds in cones (e.g., spruce, fir, pine) (SLE 4, 5, 6).

2. **Trees and forests are valuable to the environment and to human beings (SLE 1, 2).**

2.1 Trees and forests support life (e.g., purify air, release oxygen, participate in nutrient cycles) and are habitats for other living things (SLE 1, 2, 3).

2.2 Trees and forests supply us with raw materials and offer us opportunities for recreation (SLE 1).

3. **Trees grow because their leaves convert the energy in sunlight into helpful chemicals (e.g., sugars, starches) through a process known as photosynthesis (SLE 4, 6, 7).**

3.1 Trees exhibit annular growth patterns or rings around their circumference that provide a record of the conditions under which they grew (SLE 7).

4. **Human actions can enhance (e.g., tree planting) or threaten (e.g., clear-cutting) the existence of trees and forests (SLE 8, 9, 10).**

4.1 Human actions regarding forests should be guided by knowledge gained through research, investigation, and consultation (SLE 8, 9, 10).

Part E
Growing Professionally

Part

E

Sources of Professional Support

As a science educator, you should be knowledgeable about three major sources of professional support:

- **The Alberta Teachers' Association – Science Specialist Council (ATA-Science Specialist Council).**
- **The Centre for Mathematics, Science and Technology Education (CMASTE or IONCMASTE).**
- **National Science Teachers Association (NSTA).**

The **ATA– Science Specialist Council** is one of the 20 specialist councils sponsored by the Alberta Teachers' Association. Specialist councils foster the professional development of teachers who share a common curriculum interest. Full-time university students who join as student members can enjoy the benefits of publications (*The Alberta Science Education Journal and The Alberta Science Teacher*), conferences, and seminars.

The **CMASTE** began in January 1993 in the Faculty of Education at the University of Alberta. The centre was formed with the intent of promoting teaching, research and curriculum excellence in mathematics, science, and technology education. In 1999, CMASTE received a large grant from Imperial Oil and the name of the centre was changed to IONCMASTE (The Imperial Oil National Centre for Mathematics, Science and Technology Education). CMASTE offers teachers and preservice teachers access to a wide range of publications intended to support the teaching of mathematics, science, and technology in schools.

The **NSTA** (this is an American organization), founded in 1944, has as members a large number of science teachers, science supervisors, principals, academics, and science industry contacts (mostly American, but international educators are welcome to join). The NSTA produces science teaching resources for all levels, provides support documents that help teachers interpret science standards, and lobbies governments to provide support for science teachers. You should consider joining the NSTA, attend their conferences, and give serious consideration to accessing their print resources (e.g., *NSTA Pathways to the Science Standards*, 1997). Joining the NSTA will help you become a more informed and professional science teacher with a more international outlook on the profession.

Selected Websites

THE ALBERTA TEACHERS' ASSOCIATION – SCIENCE SPECIALIST COUNCIL
http://www.atasc.ab.ca
This website provides information about the council and upcoming science conferences.

THE CENTRE FOR MATHEMATICS, SCIENCE AND TECHNOLOGY EDUCATION
http://www.ioncmaste.ca
This website provides a list of publications and helpful Internet links that can be used to teach a variety of topics in the elementary program.

NATIONAL SCIENCE TEACHERS ASSOCIATION
http://www.nsta.org/
This website contains information about resources for improving science teaching, upcoming conventions, professional journals, and publications. The NSTA Pressroom feature provides copies of the latest NSTA news releases.

Alberta Science and Technology Field Trips

Field trips are an important part of science and technology learning and there are many beneficial locations you can visit with your class. These include science centres, museums, natural areas, and recycling centres. In most geographic areas you will find helpful publications that inform you about suggested locations and give you contact information for organizations that will assist you.

Selected Field Trips

Edmonton and Area

- Alberta Aviation Museum, 11410 Kingsway Ave.
- Astronomical Observatory at the University of Alberta, Physics Building.
- Big Lake, St. Albert.
- Canadian Petroleum Interpretive Centre, 2 km south of Devon on Highway 60.
- Children's Educational Wildlife Museum, 5304 97 St.
- Devonian Botanic Garden, 5 km north of Devon on Highway 60.
- Edmonton International Airport, Nisku.
- Elk Island National Park, Fort Saskatchewan.
- John Janzen Nature Centre, SW corner Fox Drive and Whitemud Drive.
- Kings University College Observatory.
- Muttart Conservatory, 9626 96a St.

- North Saskatchewan River.
- Northern Alberta Institute of Technology, 11672 106 St.
- Odyssium, 11211 142 St.
- Provincial Museum of Alberta, 12845 102 St.
- Stratchcona Wilderness Centre, Strathcona County (east of Edmonton).
- University of Alberta, 8440 112 St.
- Valley Zoo, 13315 Buena Vista Road.
- Whitemud Ravine Natural Reserve.

Calgary and Area

- Ann and Sandy Cross Conservation Area, SW of Calgary off Highway 22X.
- Bow Habitat Station at Sam Livingston Fish Hatchery, 1440 17a St. SE.
- Bow River.
- Calgary Aerospace Museum, 4629 McCall Way NE.
- Calgary International Airport, 15 km NE of downtown Calgary.
- Calgary Science Centre, 701 11 St. SW.
- Calgary Zoo, Botanical Garden, and Prehistoric Park, 1300 Zoo Road NE.
- Elbow River.
- Energeum, 640 5th Ave SW.
- Fish Creek Provincial Park, 13 km south of downtown Calgary.
- Inglewood Bird Sanctuary, 2425 9th Avenue SE.
- Nose Hill Park, NW Calgary.
- Rothney Astrophysical Observatory, Priddis.
- Southern Alberta Institute of Technology, 1301 16th Avenue NW.
- University of Calgary, 2500 University Drive NW.
- Weaselhead Glenmore Park/Glenmore Reservoir, SW Calgary.

Lethbridge and Area

- Agriculture Centre, 1st Ave South.
- Alberta Birds of Prey Centre, east of Lethbridge on Highway 3.
- Dinosaur Provincial Park, Brooks (Highway 1).
- Helen Schuler Coulee Centre, 3rd Avenue and Scenic Drive.
- St. Mary Dam, 40 km SW on Highway 5.
- Three Rivers Rock and Fossil Museum, Pincher Creek.

- Waterton Lakes National Park, SW of Lethbridge on Highway 5.

Rocky Mountains/West

- Banff National Park.
- Frank Slide Interpretive Centre.
- Jasper National Park.
- Kananaskis Country.

Central Area

- Reynolds-Alberta Museum, 2 km west of Wetaskiwin on Highway 13.
- Royal Tyrell Museum of Paleontology, Drumheller.
- OTS Heavy Oil and Science Centre, Lloydminster.

North Area

- Huestis Demonstration Forest, north of Whitecourt off Highway 32.
- Lesser Slave Lake Bird Observatory, Slave Lake.
- Oil Sands Discovery Centre, Fort McMurray.
- Swan Hills Hazardous Waste Plant, north of Swan Hills on Highway 33.

Selected Books

Huck, B. & Whiteway, D. (1998). *In Search of Ancient Alberta*. Winnipeg: Heartland Publishing.

Keirnan, M. (2003). *Reading the Rocks*. Drumheller: Royal Tyrrell Museum.

Mussieux, R. & Nelson, M. (1998). *Geological Wonders in Alberta*. Edmonton: Provincial Museum.

Reynolds, L. (1997). *Edmonton Science Fun Guide*. Edmonton: Bare Bones Publishing.

Reynolds, L. (1994). *Calgary Science Fun Guide*. Calgary: Bare Bones Publishing.

Selected Websites

EDMONTON ODYSSIUM
www.odyssium.com

EDMONTON SPACE AND SCIENCE CENTRE
www.vredmonton.com/SSC

CALGARY SCIENCE CENTRE
www.calgaryscience.ca

OILSANDS DISCOVERY CENTRE, FORT MCMURRAY
www.oilsandsdiscovery.com

PROVINCIAL PARKS
http://www1.travelalberta.com/content/parks/otherparks.cfm

ROYAL TYRRELL MUSEUM (PALEONTOLOGY)
http://www.tyrrellmuseum.com/